So you <u>really</u> want to learn

Geography
Book One

James Dale-Adcock

Series Editor: Simon Lewis

ISEB
Independent Schools
Examinations Board

www.galorepark.co.uk

GALORE PARK

Published by Galore Park Publishing Ltd
19/21 Sayers Lane, Tenterden, Kent TN30 6BW
www.galorepark.co.uk

Typography by Typetechnique, London
Illustrations by Simon Tegg and Ian Moores
Cartoons by Ian Douglass
Index compiled by Indexing Specialists (UK) Ltd

Printed by L.E.G.O. S.p.A., Italy

ISBN: 978 1 902984 72 8

First published 2007, reprinted 2009, 2010, revised 2011

Details of other Galore Park publications are available at
www.galorepark.co.uk

ISEB Revision Guides, publications and examination papers may also be
obtained from Galore Park.

Acknowledgements

OS Ordnance Survey® This product includes mapping data licensed from Ordnance Survey ® reproduced by permission of Ordnance Survey on behalf of HMSO. © Crown copyright 2007. All rights reserved. Ordnance Survey Licence number 150001477. Ordnance Survey and the OS symbol are registered trademarks and Explorer and Landranger are trademarks of the Ordnance Survey, the national mapping agency of Great Britain.

The publishers are grateful for permission to use the photographs as follows:

(T = Top, C = Centre, B = Bottom, L = Left, R = Right)

Chapter 1: p6 (TL) Tim Graham/Alamy; (TR) Stephen Finn/Alamy; (B) Martin Bond/Science Photo Library; p26 (T) Julian Nieman/Alamy; (B) Robert Morris/Alamy; p27 (T) Annie Poole/Science Photo Library; (C) Andy Sutton/Alamy; (B) Peter Bowater/Alamy; p35 The Photolibrary Wales/Alamy; **Chapter 2:** p49 Robert Brook/Science Photo Library; p51 Martin Bond/Science Photo Library; p55 Holmes Garden Photos/Alamy; p49 David Poole/Alamy; p56(T); Chris Howes/Wild Places Photography/Alamy; p61 Philippe Plailly/Eurelios/Science Photo Library; p62 Gavin Hellier/Alamy; p69 (T) G P Bowater/Alamy; (C) Y Hamel, Publiophoto Diffusion/Science Photo Library; p71 Skyscan/Science Photo Library; p72 (T) Photo Dinorwig; (B) Photo Dinorwig **Chapter 3**: p81 Ragnar Larusson/Science Photo Library; p82 Julian Hodgson; p83 Worldsat International/Science Photo Library; p84 (C) Georg Gerster/Science Photo Library; (B) Visions of America, LLC/Alamy; p87 John Russell/AFP/Getty Images; p88 (L) Geoeye/Science Photo Library; (R) Geoeye/Science Photo Library; p91 NASA/Science Photo Library; p92 (T) Bernhard Edmaier/Science Photo Library; (B) Jeremy Bishop/Science Photo Library; p93 Jeremy Bishop/Science Photo Library; p94 Stephen & Donna O'Meara/Science Photo Library; p96 Aurora Photos/Alamy; p97 (T) Caro/Alamy; (B) Colin Galloway/Alamy; p99 Jeremy Bishop/Science Photo Library; **Chapter 4**: p104 Herve Donnezan/Science Photo Library; p105 (T) David R Frazier/Science Photo Library; (B) Maximilian Stock Ltd/Science Photo Library; p109 Jiri Rezac/Alamy; p112 Martin Bond /Science Photo Library; p114 (T) Greenshoots Communications/Alamy; (B) Tim Gartside/Alamy; p115 David Martyn Hughes/Alamy; p116 Skyscan Photolibrary/Alamy; p117 Paul Thompson Images/Alamy; p118 JLImages/Alamy; p119 (T) Jon Arnold Images Ltd/Alamy; (B) Photofusion Picture Library/Alamy; p120 Jon Hicks/Alamy; p123 Mark Boulton/Alamy; p124 Photo Japan/Alamy; p126 Digiteyes/Alamy; p127 SCPhotos/alamy; p128 Picture Contact BV/Alamy; **Chapter 5**: p136 Kevin A Horgan/Science Photo Library; p137 Alan Copson City Pictures/Alamy; p138 Jon Arnold Images Ltd/Alamy; p142 Art Kowalsky/Alamy; p147 Planetary Visions Ltd/Science Photo Library; p148 Danita Delimont/Alamy; p149 Robert Harding Picture Library Ltd/Alamy; p152 Alan Copson City Pictures/Alamy; p153 picturedimensions/Alamy; p155 Robert Harding Picture Library Ltd/Alamy; p156 G P Bowater/Alamy

Contents

Chapter 4: Economic activities

Chapter 5: Location knowledge

Appendix 1: Ordnance Survey map keys

Introduction

This textbook is written for Year 7 pupils and, together with *So you really want to learn Geography Book 2,* forms a Key Stage 3 course which is particularly suited to those preparing for ISEB Common Entrance Exams at 13+. Within this course every aspect of the syllabus is covered in detail and tested with appropriate questions which conclude each section or chapter.

Each chapter is punctuated by key words which are highlighted in bold. Definitions of these key words can be found in the topic glossaries at the end of each chapter. At the end of each chapter a group activity/game is suggested. These activities not only stimulate pupils but are very effective at reinforcing skills and knowledge they will have learned in the preceding chapter.

The new Key Stage 3 concepts seek to encourage a broadening of pupils' knowledge, skills and understanding of the world around them. Throughout the *So you really want to learn Geography* series, I have sought to emphasise these concepts. By the end of the two books pupils should have the knowledge to discuss and understand how they might contribute to their futures; not only in terms of understanding interactions between people and places, at local, national and international levels, but also how natural and man-made events can affect social, economic and environmental relationships.

If you are using this book for ISEB Common Entrance you should be aware that the revised syllabus (2010) places a significant emphasis on learning theory and skills based on topic case studies. This approach permeates this textbook with every opportunity taken to relate theory and skills to detailed contemporary examples.

When the syllabus demands knowledge of an example, the textbook clearly marks this case study as a **syllabus example**. If a case study is not required by the syllabus but is included to reinforce theory we have marked it as an **extra example**.

We have also included a section on fieldwork skills. Part B in Chapter 1 covers the skills required to conduct and present the results of fieldwork projects (worth 20% of the marks at Common Entrance).

James Dale-Adcock

Additional resources

All textbooks in the Galore Park Geography series have answer books, which can be particularly useful for parents wishing to aid pupils with their studies.

The *Geography ISEB Revision Guide* is an invaluable companion to this series as pupils prepare for their Common Entrance exams.

Blank maps of Britain, Europe and the world to help with revision are available for download from the Galore Park website, www.galorepark.co.uk

Chapter 1: Geographical skills

In this chapter we will be looking at some key skills you will need to master in order to become a great geographer. We will start with mapwork skills and then we will turn our attention to all the things you should know about collecting, recording and presenting data from your fieldwork studies.

Part A: Mapwork skills

Of all the topics you will study in Geography, mapwork may be the most obviously useful. One day you may need to be able to read a map in order to find your way down a mountain, not just to pass an exam! Geography exams require pupils to be able to read and use Ordnance Survey maps at different scales. In this chapter we will study the following:

● Four figure grid references to identify features on a map.

● Six figure grid references to identify features on a map.

● Understanding instructions relating to the eastings and northings that dissect a map vertically and horizontally.

● Working out the direction of one map feature to another, and how to measure the distance between them.

● Recognising the height of places on a map and how to visualise what the landscape would look like if you were at ground level.

1.1 The OS map and using grid references

What does an OS map look like?
You will need to be able to use an Ordnance Survey map (OS map), so let us start by looking at what we would expect to see on an OS map.

Title
Always read the title of a map before you start. It will give you a good idea of the information it contains. (See Fig. 1.1.1).

OS Landranger Map 190

Bude & Clovelly
Boscastle & Holsworthy

1 : 50 000 scale

Fig. 1.1.1: Title and scale on an OS map

Scale

In the top right-hand corner of the OS map there is a **scale** (see Fig. 1.1.1). The maps you use in class will be at a scale of either 1:25 000 or 1:50 000, meaning that distances on the map will be either 25 000 times or 50 000 times larger in real life.

Grid squares, eastings and northings

OS maps are divided up into squares with blue sides, called **grid squares** (see Fig. 1.1.2). The vertical and horizontal thin blue lines create these squares.

The vertical thin blue lines are called **eastings**. The horizontal thin blue lines are called **northings**.

Each easting and northing is given a two digit number for identification. This number can be found at the end of each line. These numbers are used to give a four or six figure grid references (we will discuss these in detail in the next section). Look at Fig. 1.1.9 (page 9), which shows an extract from an OS map at a scale of 1:50 000. It shows nine grid squares which are made up of four eastings running vertically and four northings running horizontally.

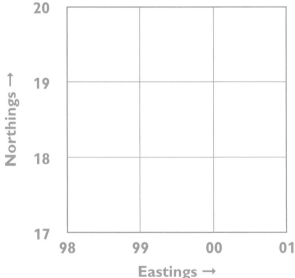

Fig. 1.1.2: Grid squares

Which way is north?

Compass directions are vital for finding your way around a map. On all OS maps, north is always straight towards the top of the map. This makes giving and receiving directions straightforward.

Scale bar

At the bottom of all OS maps you will find a **scale bar**. The scale bar allows you quickly to work out distances between different points on a map and to find the size, height and dimensions of physical features shown on the map.

The scale bar in Fig. 1.1.3 is for a 1:25 000 scale map. At this scale 1 cm on the map represents 25 000 cm on the ground (i.e. 250 metres or 0.25 kilometres).

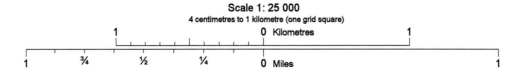

Fig. 1.1.3: Scale bar for a 1:25 000 scale map

The scale bar in Fig. 1.1.4 is for a 1:50 000 scale map. At this scale 1 cm on the map represents 50 000 cm on the ground (i.e. 500 metres or 0.5 kilometres)

Fig. 1.1.4: Scale bar for a 1:50 000 scale map

Key

The **key**, or legend, on a map will help you unlock the information stored in the symbols and colours on a map. It is important to understand the symbols and their meanings. The key will help you identify roads, railways, boundaries, features such as post offices and churches, agricultural, industrial and geographical features, tourist and leisure information and so on. See Figs. 1.1.5 and 1.1.6.

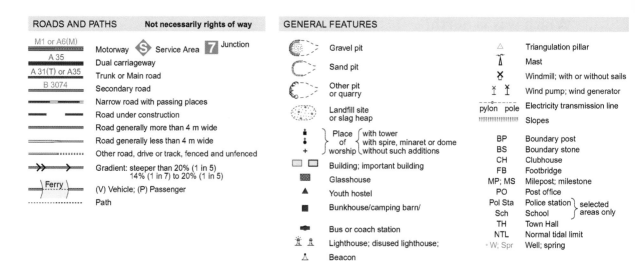

ROADS AND PATHS — Not necessarily rights of way

M1 or A6(M)	Motorway — Service Area — Junction
A 35	Dual carriageway
A 31(T) or A35	Trunk or Main road
B 3074	Secondary road
	Narrow road with passing places
	Road under construction
	Road generally more than 4 m wide
	Road generally less than 4 m wide
	Other road, drive or track, fenced and unfenced
	Gradient: steeper than 20% (1 in 5)
	14% (1 in 7) to 20% (1 in 5)
Ferry	(V) Vehicle; (P) Passenger
	Path

GENERAL FEATURES

	Gravel pit
	Sand pit
	Other pit or quarry
	Landfill site or slag heap
	Place of worship {with tower / with spire, minaret or dome / without such additions}
	Building; important building
	Glasshouse
	Youth hostel
	Bunkhouse/camping barn/
	Bus or coach station
	Lighthouse; disused lighthouse;
	Beacon

△	Triangulation pillar
	Mast
	Windmill; with or without sails
	Wind pump; wind generator
pylon pole	Electricity transmission line
	Slopes
BP	Boundary post
BS	Boundary stone
CH	Clubhouse
FB	Footbridge
MP; MS	Milepost; milestone
PO	Post office
Pol Sta	Police station } selected areas only
Sch	School
TH	Town Hall
NTL	Normal tidal limit
W; Spr	Well; spring

Glasshouse

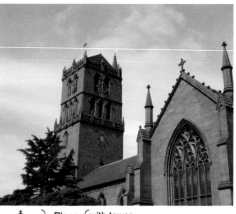

Place of worship {with tower / with spire, minaret or dome / without such additions}

Lighthouse; disused lighthouse

Fig 1.1.5: Key 1:25 000 OS map with examples of features

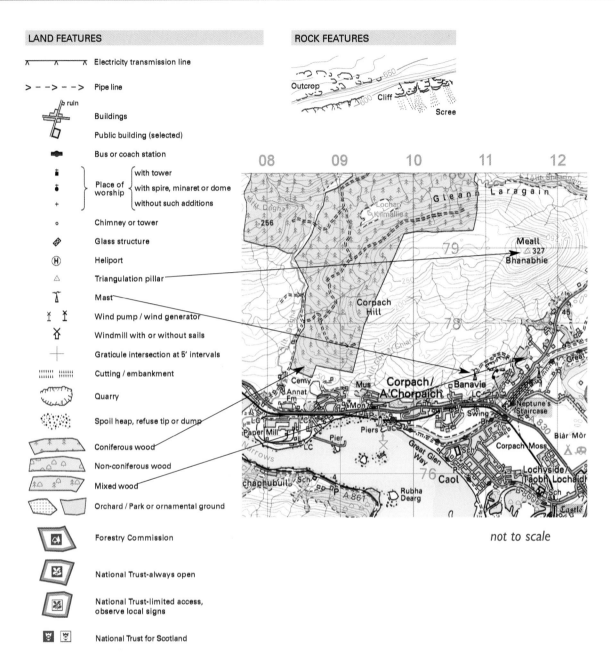

Fig. 1.1.6: Key 1:50 000 OS map of Fort William with map extract

Can you spot any more of these symbols on the map?

The key will also help you to identify urban and rural land use. Particular features in the key may be related to the countryside or town. For example, the symbols in Fig. 1.1.7 tell you about the land use around Godshill (see Fig. 1.1.9, page 9).

| Building; important building | Buildings around the main road form the village of Godshill |
| Glasshouse | Glasshouse, (greenhouses) at Little Budbridge Farm |

Fig. 1.1.7: Land features from a key

Features of urban landscapes are also represented by symbols on the OS map. Some relate to modes of transport, for example: junctions of main roads, railways, ports and airports. The symbols in Fig. 1.1.8 tell you about the land use around Exeter (see Fig. 1.1.13, page 14).

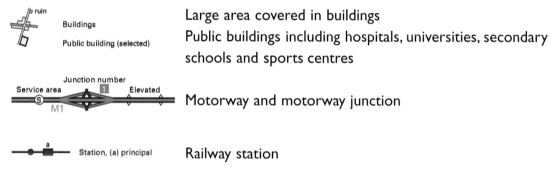

Large area covered in buildings
Public buildings including hospitals, universities, secondary schools and sports centres

Motorway and motorway junction

Railway station

Fig. 1.1.8: Land features from a key

The complete keys for both the 1:25 000 and 1:50 000 maps can be found in Appendix 1 (pages 161–4). Try to familiarise yourself with as many of the symbols as you can.

Four figure grid references

Four figure grid references allow us to identify a specific grid square by using the reference numbers of the eastings and northings.

Let us look at an example:

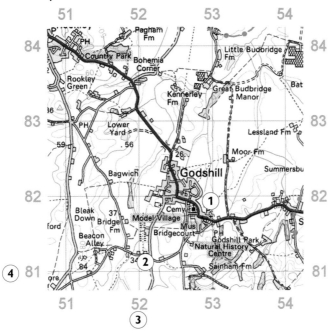

Fig. 1.1.9: Four figure grid references (1:50 000)

Look at Fig. 1.1.9, which is an OS map extract of the Isle of Wight. We want to identify which grid square the *model village* is in.

Step 1:   Find the *model village* which is to the south of *Godshill*.

Step 2:   Go to the bottom left hand corner of that grid square.

Step 3:   Follow the easting (the vertical line) from this point to the end of the line (either at the top or the bottom) where you will find its two digit reference number. Write down this number: 52.

Step 4:   Return to the bottom left hand corner of the grid square containing the *model village*. Follow the northing (the horizontal line) from this point to the end of the line where you will find its two digit reference number: 81. Write down this number next to the previous number.

Step 5:   You should now have a four digit number – 5281 – which is the four figure grid reference for the grid square containing the *model village*. Always write the easting reference first, followed by the northing reference.

Fig. 1.1.10: Four figure grid references (1:50 000)

Let us now look at what you do if you are given a grid reference.

Look at Fig. 1.1.10. The grid square you need to find is 5183.

Step 1: Split the grid reference 5183 into two parts: 51 and 83.

Step 2: The first two digit number refers to the easting. Find easting 51 along the bottom of the map and put one finger of your right hand on it.

Step 3: The second two digit number refers to the northing. Find northing 83 on the left side of the map and put one finger of your left hand on it.

Step 4: Move your right finger vertically and your left finger horizontally along the grid lines until they meet. This is the bottom left hand corner of the grid square you need to find: 5183.

The bottom left hand corner is the meeting point of easting and northing, whether you are giving or receiving a four figure grid reference. Don't forget the bottom left hand corner rule. Use the saying 'go along the corridor before you go up the stairs' to remind yourself that the easting reference always comes before the northing reference.

Six figure grid references

The problem with four figure grid references is that you can only narrow down a place on the map to one grid square. A grid square on an OS map is one square kilometre, so if you want to pinpoint the exact location of something small such as a telephone box, you need to be much more accurate. This problem is overcome by dividing the sides of each grid square into tenths, which then gives you an extra digit to the two digit easting and two digit northing numbers. When they are put together, they create a **six figure grid reference**. Don't forget the bottom left hand corner rule and use the saying 'go along the corridor before you go up the stairs' to remind yourself that the easting reference always comes before the northing reference.

Let us now look at what we do when we want to tell someone exactly where something is on a map. Look at Fig. 1.1.11 (page 12). You want to identify where precisely the *church* is in Godshill.

Step 1:   Find the *church* symbol in Godshill (the symbol for a *church* is a black square with a + sign on the top of it ♦).

Step 2:   Identify the four figure grid reference for the grid square containing the *church*. Your answer should read 5281. If it doesn't, look again at how to do four figure grid references.

Step 3:   To find the extra easting digit, go to the bottom left hand corner of grid square 5281 and imagine nine extra eastings running vertically across the square. These are not normally drawn on maps but they have been shown in Fig. 1.1.11 to help you. How many lines across do you have to go before reaching the *church*? You should have counted 7. Write this number after the first part of the four figure grid reference (52<u>7</u>).

Step 4:   To find the extra northing digit, return to the bottom left hand corner of the grid square containing the *church*. This time imagine nine extra northings running horizontally up the square. How many lines up do you have to go before reaching the *church*? You should have counted 8. Write this number after the second part of the four figure grid reference (81<u>8</u>).

Step 5:   Put the two sets of numbers together, eastings first and then northings. You now have a six figure grid reference for the *church* in Godshill which should read 527818.

Fig. 1.1.11: Six figure grid references (1:50 000)

Fig. 1.1.12: Six figure grid references (1:50 000)

Let us now look at what you do if you are given a six figure grid reference.

Now look at Fig. 1.1.12. Use the following steps to identify the feature at grid reference 529818.

Step 1: Divide the grid reference 529818 into two parts (529 and 818) and underline the first two digits of each set of numbers to find the four figure grid reference first (529 and 818 tells us that the four figure grid reference is **5281**).

Step 2: Find the four figure grid reference and put one finger of your right hand and one finger of your left hand on the bottom left hand corner of this grid square.

Step 3: Look again at the first set of numbers: 529. The third digit, the one you have not underlined, tells you how many imaginary extra eastings you need to move across the grid square. Imagine nine extra eastings running across the square and move the finger of your right hand across the grid square to imaginary easting 9. These imaginary eastings are not normally drawn on maps but are shown in Fig. 1.1.12 to help you. Keep your finger on this point.

Step 4: Look again at the second set of numbers, <u>81</u>8. The third digit, the one you have not underlined, tells you how many imaginary extra northings you need to move up the grid square. Imagine nine extra northings running up the square and move the finger of your left hand up the grid square to imaginary northing 8. These imaginary northings are not normally drawn on maps but are shown in Fig. 1.1.12 to help you.

Step 5: Now move your right finger vertically and your left finger horizontally along these imaginary grid lines until they meet. Your fingers should meet at the letter P, which represents a *post office*.

The dotted lines on Figs. 1.1.11 and 1.1.12 represent the imaginary eastings and northings that you need to create in your head when you are doing six figure grid references. They are not drawn on real OS maps, because these extra grid lines would cover all the other information the map shows.

Exercise 1A

All questions refer to Fig. 1.1.13, the map extract of Exeter below.

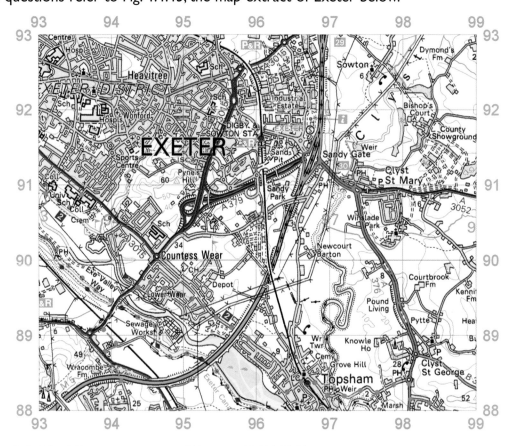

Fig. 1.1.13: OS map extract of Exeter (1:50 000)

You may need to refer to the 1:50 000 key in Appendix 1, pages 163–4 to find the answers to these questions.

1. Name a feature you can find on the map of Exeter in the following grid squares.
   (a) 9488
   (b) 9590
   (c) 9892
   (d) 9691

2. There are five schools on the map of Exeter. Give the four figure grid reference for each of them.

3. What would you find at the following six figure grid references?
   (a) 967883
   (b) 946903
   (c) 989897
   (d) 932927

4. Give the six figure grid reference for any telephone box you find on the map of Exeter.

5. Which form of transport might you be using if you were at the following grid references?
   (a) 952905
   (b) 933907
   (c) 966883
   (d) 933883

Extension question

6. Look again at the 1:50 000 OS map key in Appendix 1 (pages 163–4) under the land features section. You should see there are three different symbols for places of worship. Give the six figure grid references of any places of worship you find on the map extract of Exeter.

1.2 Identifying direction and measuring distances

Which way is it?

Maps are most often used to help people find a place or destination. Think about a long car journey you made to somewhere you had not been to before. If you did not have a sat nav system, you probably used a road map to work out which route to follow. If you looked out of the window on that journey you would have probably noticed road signs naming towns, roads and directions.

M1 NORTH
Nottingham

Instead of using words such as up, down, left or right to give directions, we use the directions of the four point compass: north, east, south and west. It may help you to remember them by learning the rhyme 'Never Eat Shredded Wheat'. A more accurate direction can be given if we take the four point compass a step further and add directions in between the four points to make the eight point compass (see Fig. 1.2.1). Notice, when using the extra directions of the eight point compass, we always say north or south first, not east or west (e.g. north-east not east-north; south-west not west-south). To make giving and receiving directions simple on OS maps, north is always at the top of the map.

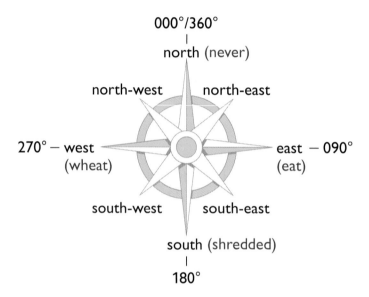

Fig. 1.2.1: Eight point compass with bearings

For even greater accuracy when giving very precise directions, the eight point compass can be broken down into the 360 degrees of a circle which we call **bearings**. You will have used a protractor during maths lessons and should know that a circle is split into 360 degrees. North is at 000° or 360°, east is at 090°, south is at 180° and west is at 270°. Mountaineers and orienteering groups use compasses with bearings on them to find their way to given points, a vital skill on difficult terrain or in bad weather conditions. Bearings are also used by the armed forces.

Be careful always to read a question carefully when being asked to give or receive directions. Look at Fig. 1.2.2 (page 17). 'Which direction is it from A to B?' and 'Which direction is A from B?' are two different questions which look very similar but have two different answers. Look at where the question says 'from'; it may help to imagine yourself standing at that point on the map.

(i) Which direction is it from A to B?
The arrow here is pointing from A to B in a northerly direction, so the answer is north.

(ii) Which direction is A from B?
The arrow is pointing from B to A in a southerly direction, so the answer is south.

Fig. 1.2.2: Is it always as easy as A to B?

What is meant by the scale of the map?

All Ordnance Survey maps have a **scale ratio**. This ratio tells us how much larger distances marked on a map are in real life. Therefore if the scale on the map was 1:10, distances on the map would actually be ten times bigger in real life. The OS maps you are most likely to use have scale ratios of 1:25 000 or 1:50 000. A 1:25 000 map has a higher ratio (is a larger scale) than a 1:50 000 map which is a smaller scale and less detailed. The scale ratio is always written on the bottom of the map. The grid lines on OS maps do not change with the scale; a grid square on any OS map at any scale always covers one square kilometre on the ground.

Below the scale ratio at the bottom of any OS map you will find the scale bar. Look at the map extract of the Isle of Wight on page 32 and find the scale ratio and scale bar. The scale bar is used to help find distances between places on the map, which are normally measured in kilometres, not miles. If you place your ruler on the scale bar you will be able to see how many centimetres on the map represent one kilometre. The map of the Isle of Wight is at a scale of 1:50 000, so distances on this map are 50 000 times bigger in real life. One centimetre on this map represents half a kilometre (500 metres) in real life. Now look at the map extract of the Peak District on page 34 and find the scale ratio and scale bar. This map is at a scale of 1:25 000, so distances on this map are 25 000 times bigger in real life and one centimetre represents a quarter of a kilometre (250 metres).

Using the scale bar to measure distances

Measuring the distance between two points on any OS map in a straight line, or as the crow flies, is simple. First of all use the scale bar to work out the value of one centimetre on the map. It will be either half a kilometre on 1:50 000 scale maps, or a quarter of a kilometre on 1:25 000 scale maps. Next use your ruler to measure the distance between the two points, giving you a measurement in centimetres (see Fig. 1.2.3 on page 19). Divide your answer by 2 if you are reading from a 1:50 000 map and by 4 if you are reading from a 1:25 000 map to get a measurement in kilometres.

Scale	1 cm on the map represents	To find distance in kilometres divide your measurement by
1:50 000	$\frac{1}{2}$ km	2
1:25 000	$\frac{1}{4}$ km	4

Look again at the map extract of the Isle of Wight on page 32. If you measure the distance on the map between the church in Godshill (527818) and the church in Wroxall (551799), in a straight line, you should get an answer of 6 centimetres. Divide this by 2 because it is a 1:50 000 map, to give you an answer of 3 kilometres.

1:50 000   6 cm on map ÷ 2 = 3 km

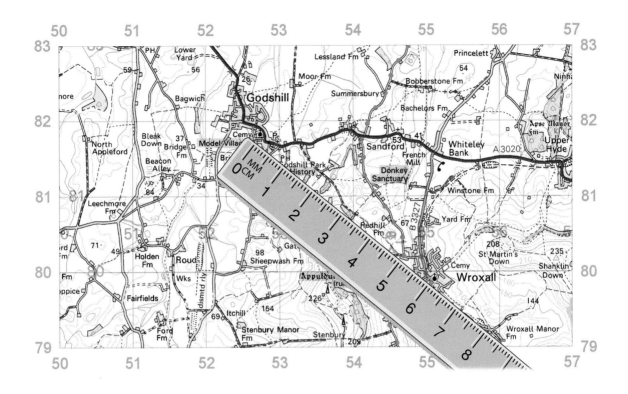

Fig. 1.2.3: Measuring distances as the crow flies (1:50 000)

Measuring distances by road

Often you will need to measure distances that are not in a straight line, such as the distance between two places along a road. In this case you can use a piece of paper to measure the distance along the road between the two places in question. Line up the edge of the piece of paper from the starting point along the first piece of road. Make a mark on the paper next to the starting point. Follow the edge of paper along the first section of road until the road changes direction and then make a mark at this point. Holding the piece of paper steady at that point turn it until it lines up along the next piece of road. Continue this process until you reach your destination, making your final mark at this point. You should end up with marks all along the edge of the paper.

Using a ruler, measure the distance from the first mark to the last mark to get an answer in centimetres. Then convert this measurement into kilometres using the scale bar as we have just practised.

Let us look at an example based on the OS map of the Peak District (1:25 000) on page 34.

Measure the distance from the church in Castleton to the church in Hope via Pindale Farm

Step 1: Measure the distance along the yellow minor road from the church in Castleton (150829) to Peveril Castle. Because of the bend in the road, you will need to mark first from the church to the bend, and then from the bend to the castle. Mark the position of the church and the position of the castle on your piece of paper.

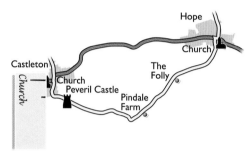

Step 2: Now move the paper until it lies between the castle and Pindale Farm, keeping the marked position of the castle on the castle symbol on the map.

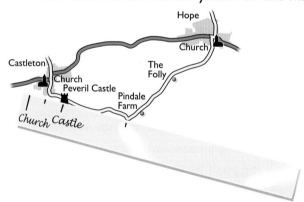

Step 3: Now measure the distance between Pindale Farm, crossing the railway line towards Hope to the Folly. Again, line up the piece of paper and mark the position of the Folly.

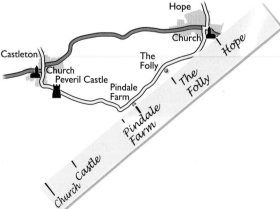

Step 4: Move the paper again and line it up on the road between the Folly and the church in Hope.

Step 5: Then place the piece of paper on a ruler and read off the measurement in centimetres.

Step 6: Finally, refer to the scale bar on the map and calculate the distance between the two points in kilometres.

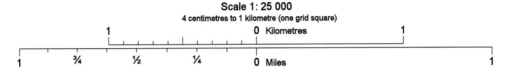

In this instance you should have measured **12** centimetres. Divide by 4 because it is a 1:25 000 scale map to give you a distance between the two points of 3 kilometres.

Using scale to measure area

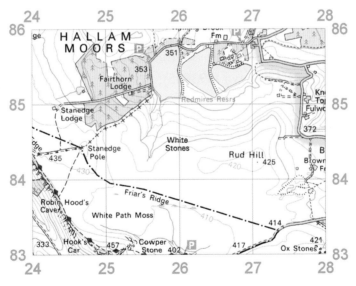

Fig. 1.2.4: OS map extract of Hallam Moor near Sheffield (1:50 000)

If we know what distance a centimetre represents on an OS map, whether it is a 1:25 000 or 1:50 000 map, we can use this information to work out areas as well as distances.

Fig. 1.2.4 (above) is taken from a 1:50 000 map extract of Sheffield. Can you work out the size of area it is showing? Remember that each grid square is always worth one square kilometre whatever the scale of the OS map. There are two ways to calculate the area in this case. Either you could count up the number of grid squares, which in this case is 12, so the area covered is 12 square kilometres. Or you could multiply the number of grid squares going eastwards (4), by the number going northwards (3) (4 km x 3 km = 12 km²) to give the same answer of 12 square kilometres.

Sometimes you may have to estimate the size of irregular areas. Look at Fig. 1.2.4 again (page 21). Imagine you were asked to estimate the total area covered by woodland on the map. Rather than spending a large amount of time taking difficult measurements it would be better to estimate how many grid squares the woodland might fill if it were all put together. A fair estimate in this example would be one grid square, giving you an answer of one square kilometre of woodland.

Exercise 1B

Look at the map extract of the Isle of Wight on page 32.

1. (a) In which direction does the village of Godshill (5282) lie from the village of Wroxall (5579)?

    (b) What direction is it from the village of Godshill (5282) to the village of Wroxall (5579)?

2. (a) How far is it as the crow flies from the public house in Rookley (512840) to the train station in Sandown (593845)?
    (b) Which direction would you be going in if you travelled the route in part (a)?

3. (a) How far is it as the crow flies from the post office at Whitwell (522778) to the zoo (552843)?
    (b) Describe the route you would take by road to get from the post office at Whitwell to the zoo. Name the roads you would take and any changes in direction you would have to make.
    (c) If you followed this route along the road, how far would it be?

Look at the map extract of the Peak District on page 34.

4. (a) How far is it as the crow flies from Teak Cliff Cavern (134832) to Bagshawe Cavern (172808)?
    (b) Which direction would you be going in if you travelled the route in part (a)?

5. (a) How far would you walk if you walked along the Limestone Way from where it enters the map (130800) to where it ends at Peveril Castle (150827)?
    (b) Which direction would you be walking in if you followed this route on the Limestone Way?

Extension question

6. Look again at the map extract of the Peak District on page 34. Using your circular protractor give bearings in degrees for the following directions.
    (a) From the mill (178820) to Marsh Farm (164835).
    (b) From the camping and caravan site (178830) to Eccles House Farm (174827).
    (c) From the car park (140828) to the Training and Conference centre (147835).

1.3 Height and shape of land on OS maps

What a relief!

The word **relief** in Geography refers to the shape and height of the land. What is the relief like around your home or school? Is it flat land, or gently rolling hills, or do you live in a mountainous area? Maps are two dimensional (i.e. flat) so, in order to show the relief of the land, **cartographers** (people who make maps) had to invent methods of displaying height on a two-dimensional surface. Some maps, and particularly atlases, use darker colours to shade higher land. This method is not used on OS maps. Instead **spot heights** and **contour lines** are used to indicate both the height and the shape of the land.

Spot heights and triangulation pillars

Spot heights are represented by a small black dot with the exact height at that point written next to it. The height is always given in metres above sea level. Many, but not all, spot heights are located on roads because it is easier to measure height from an even surface. Look at Fig. 1.3.1 (page 24) taken from a map of Fort William in Scotland. Look carefully and you should be able to find at least six spot heights such as the one marked 256 at grid reference 079793.

Look now at grid reference 116789. Here you will find a spot height with a blue triangle around it which is called a **triangulation pillar**. A triangulation pillar indicates that this is the highest point in the area, therefore it is often at the top of a mountain. There can be more than one triangulation pillar on an OS map extract but they will not be located close to each other. Look at the map extract of the Isle of Wight on page 32 and you will find that there are four triangulation pillars spread across the map.

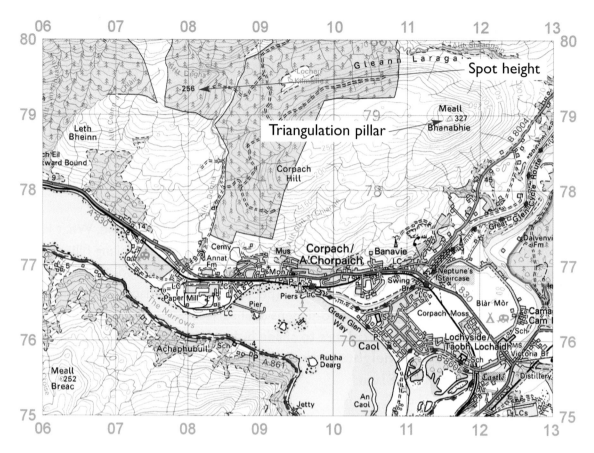

Fig. 1.3.1: OS map extract of Fort William (1:50 000)

Contour lines and relief features

Spot heights can only show the height of the land at one specific point. They cannot show the height of the land over a large area and they cannot show the shape of the land at all. Cartographers therefore use contour lines for these purposes. Contour lines are thin brown lines which join areas of equal height on the map, so if you were able to follow accurately the route of the same contour line on the ground you would be walking without going uphill or downhill.

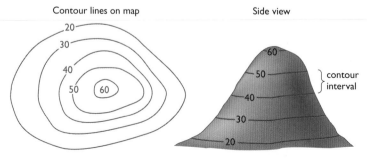

Fig. 1.3.2: Contour lines

Fig. 1.3.2 on the previous page shows how contour lines are represented on a map and what the feature looks like from the side view. The space between the contour lines is called the **contour interval**. Contour lines usually increase in intervals of 10 metres. The height of any contour line can be found by following the line until you get to a figure. These are given in metres above sea level. There may not be a figure on the line being checked but there will be one above and below which will indicate the value of the relevant line.

Now look at Fig. 1.3.3A below. The closer the contour lines are together the steeper the slope will be. The angle of the slope is called the **gradient**. A steep gradient (i.e. the land is increasing in height quickly over a short distance) is represented by contour lines packed tightly together. A gentle gradient (i.e. the land is increasing in height slowly over a longer distance) is represented by contour lines which are spread further apart.

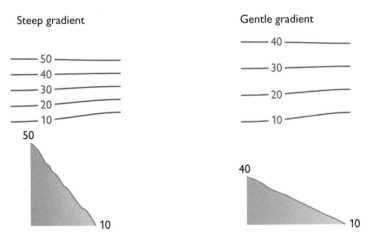

Fig. 1.3.3A: Gradients

Look at grid square 1178 in Fig. 1.3.1 (page 24). This is a very steep slope indicated by the tightly packed lines with a peak of 327 metres above sea level. The triangulation pillar shows it is the highest peak in the area. Use Fig. 1.3.1 to identify other examples of steep and gentle gradients.

Contour lines, however, are able to show more than just height and gradient. They have distinctive patterns which can be recognised. These patterns and the land shapes they represent are called **relief features**.

Round top hills (Fig. 1.3.3B on page 26) are shown by circular contour lines increasing in height steadily towards the peak of the hill or mountain. Look at grid square 5873 in the map extract on page 33 for a good example of a round top hill.

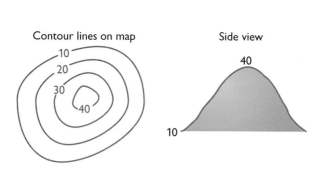

Fig. 1.3.3B: A round top hill

The contour pattern will be the same for a hollow circular depression but values will decrease towards the centre.

Flat top hills (Fig. 1.3.3C) are similar to round top hills at the base with the contour lines becoming more spread out or disappearing towards the centre of the circular shape as the hill flattens at the top. Look at grid square 5582 on the map of the Isle of Wight on page 32 to see a good example of a flat top hill.

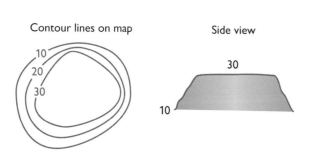

Fig. 1.3.3C: A flat top hill

Valleys (Fig. 1.3.3D on page 27) are illustrated on maps by a 'V' shaped pattern of contour lines pointing towards the top of the valley or source of any stream or river flowing in the valley. Look at grid square 0977 in Fig. 1.3.1 (page 24) for good examples of valleys showing the distinctive pattern of contour lines. Can you find any other examples of valleys in any other grid squares in Fig. 1.3.1 (page 24)?

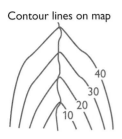
Contour lines on map

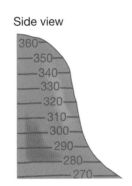
Side view

Fig. 1.3.3D: Valley

Escarpment (Fig 1.3.3E) – this often indicates a change between two physical features (for example between a valley and a **plateau**) and involves a sharp, steep slope or cliff.

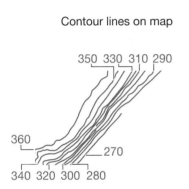
Contour lines on map

Side view

Fig. 1.3.3E: Escarpment

Ridge (Figure 1.3.3F) – this is a feature forming a long, high crest for some distance.

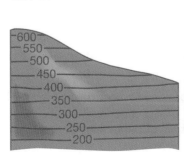
Contour lines on map

Side view

Fig. 1.3.3F: Ridge

Sketch section drawings

A sketch section is a drawing from an OS map that shows the shape and main features of the land at ground level. To draw a sketch section, you will need to locate a suitable section on an OS map and then visualise the relief using the contour lines. Draw a line to show how the height of the land varies between, for example, two eastings. Mark any features such as rivers and roads that cross the section.

Look at Fig. 1.3.4 below. It shows a sketch section looking north between easting 54 and easting 55 along northing 79 on the map of the Isle of Wight on page 32. The sketch section shows how the relief varies from easting 54 to easting 55. It also shows what you would see in front of you, gathered from looking at the contour lines and also **physical features** such as a byway, a narrow road (part of the cycle route), farm buildings, a river and a secondary road.

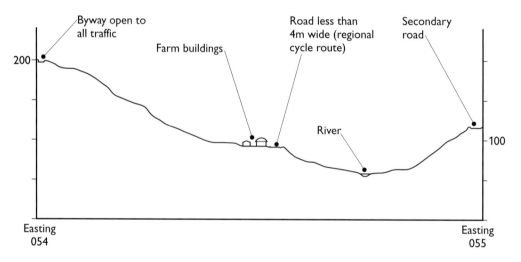

Fig. 1.3.4: A sketch section drawing

Cross section drawings

A cross section drawing shows a section of the landscape as if it had been cut through with a knife. A cross section enables you to see exactly the relief features of a map. Cross sections are often drawn along a northing or an easting, although sometimes it may be more useful to take a particular section, for example through an unusual feature.

We have already seen how a strip of paper can be used to calculate the distance along a route (see page 20). The marks made on the paper showed the changes in direction on the route. Similarly, to draw a cross section, use a strip of paper to mark out the changes in height of the landscape. Draw a line on the map where you want to do the cross section, then lay the strip of paper on the line and mark off the contour lines.

Clearly label the beginning and end of the cross section (using, for example, A and B) with their heights, and any features that your section crosses (see Fig. 1.3.5).

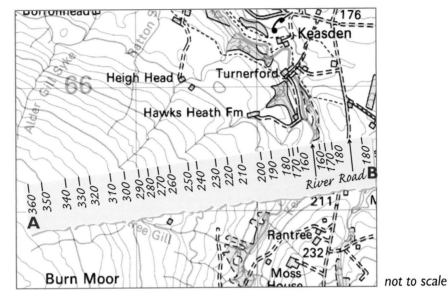

not to scale

Fig. 1.3.5: Preparing to draw a cross section

Now prepare a grid on graph paper with the x axis the same length as your section line, and the contour heights on the y axis.

Place your piece of paper at the bottom of the grid and transfer your marks onto the grid, taking care to put a dot at the correct height on the y axis. Join the dots together to form the outline of the cross section (on Fig. 1.3.6, three of the contour points have guidelines to show you how to line up your dots; you do not need to put these dotted lines on your cross section).

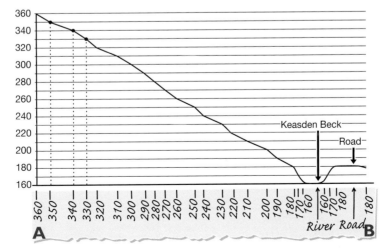

Fig. 1.3.6: A cross section drawing

Exercise 1C

1. Look at Fig. 1.3.7 below:

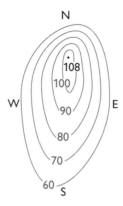

Fig. 1.3.7: Relief features example

   (a) In which direction would you climb this hill if you wanted a short vigorous walk? Give reasons for your answer.

   (b) In which direction would you climb this hill if you wanted a long easy walk? Give reasons for your answer.

   (c) When you reach the top, how high would you be?

2. Refer to the map extract of the Isle of Wight on page 32:
   (a) What is the height of the land at grid reference 555826?
   (b) What relief feature can you identify in this grid square?

3. On the map extract of the Isle of Wight on page 32, look at grid square 5680.
   (a) What is the highest point in this grid square?
   (b) Give the six figure grid reference of this point and say how you know it is the highest point.

Extension question

4. Choose a grid square from the map extract of the Peak District on page 34 and draw a sketch section of the relief viewed to the north. Set it out in the style of Fig. 1.3.4 (page 28).

End of section activity

Playing grid reference bingo is a great way of improving the speed at which you perform accurate grid references. To begin the game, you will need an OS map and ten small counters. Spread the counters randomly on the map and work out the grid references of each of the counters. The teacher writes some grid references on the board. Remove a counter from your map every time the correct grid reference appears on the board. The first person to remove three counters (or whatever number your teacher chooses) from the map should shout 'bingo' and he or she is the winner!

SHANKLIN

Little Stairs Point

Shanklin Chine

Horse Ledge

Luccombe Chine

Luccombe Bay

DUNNOSE

Monks Bay

Horseshoe Bay

Bonchurch

VENTNOR

Nansen Hill 221

Upper Bonchurch

IRB Sta (summer only)

Leisure Centre

Schs

Borthwood Fm

Isle of Wight Airport

Cheverton Fm

Merrie Gardens

Landguard Manor

Ninham

Upper Hyde

St Martin's Down

St Boniface Down

Ventnor

Winford

Queen's Bower

Bigbury Fm

Apse Heath

Apse Manor

Shanklin Down

Wroxall Manor Fm

Wroxall

Lowtherville

Mus

Bathingbourne

A 3056

Branstone

Princelett

Whiteley Bank

Winstone Fm

Yard Fm

Cemy

Steephill

Hale Common

Zoo

Bobberstone Fm

Bachelors Fm

French Mill

Donkey Sanctuary

B 3327

Redhill Fm

Appuldurcombe (ruin)

Stenbury Down

Week Down

Rew Fm

Hale Manor

Redways

Little Budbridge Fm

Great Budbridge Manor

Lessland Fm

Moor Fm

Summersbury

Godshill Park Natural History Centre

Seinham Fm

Gatcliff Fm

Obelisk

Stenbury Manor Fm

Nettlecombe

Week Down

Merstone

Kennerley Fm

Godshill

Bridgecourt

Model Village

Sheepwash Fm

Itchill

Whitwell

Dean Fm

Pagham Fm

Bohemia Corner

Lower Yard

Bagwich

Bleak Down Fm

Beacon Alley

Rough Wks

Holden Fm

Ford Fm

Southford

Bierley

Kingates

Jobsons Fm

Rookley

Rookley Green

North Appleford Fm

Fairfields

Leechmore Fm

Wydcombe

Strathwell Park

Bierley Head Down

The Hermitage

OS map extract of the Isle of Wight

Scale 1: 50 000

2 centimetres to 1 kilometre (one grid square)

2 1 0 Kilometres 1 2 3

1 ½ 0 Miles 1 2

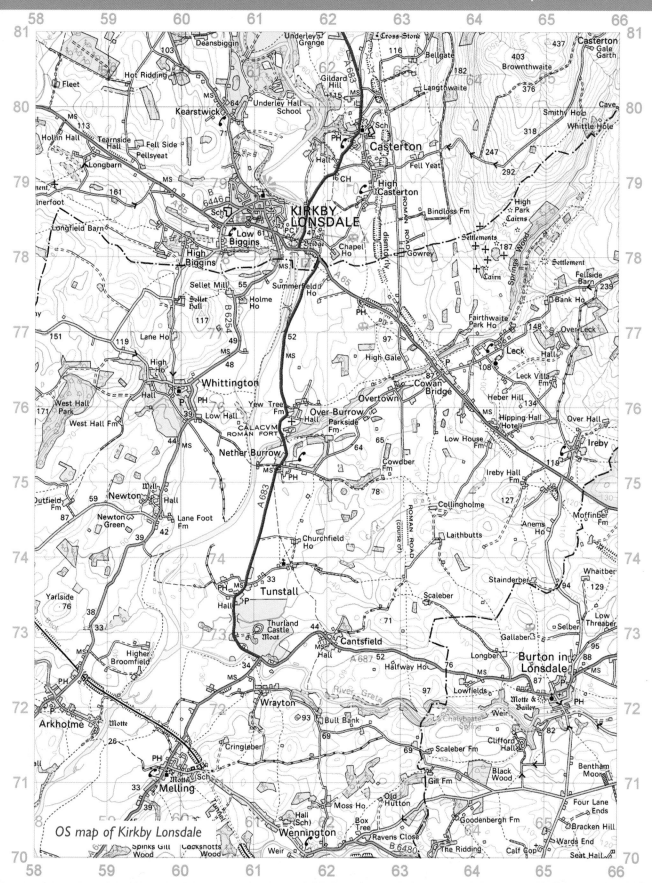

OS map of Kirkby Lonsdale

OS map extract of the Peak District

Scale 1: 25 000

4 centimetres to 1 kilometre (one grid square)

1   0 Kilometres   1

Part B: Fieldwork skills

1.4 The fieldwork study

In this section we are going to look at the skills needed to conduct a fieldwork study. You may have acquired some of these skills through other subjects, particularly Science. At Common Entrance the fieldwork study is worth 20% of the final mark for geography.

What is a fieldwork study?

Fieldwork study has long been used in the development of geographical ideas. Many of the very early geographers were in fact explorers who observed the world around them, recorded what they saw and then tried to make sense of it all. For pupils nowadays, direct hands-on experience is a good way to improve observation skills and to reinforce and develop a better understanding of the geographical processes and theories learnt in the classroom. You may do your fieldwork in a group or individually.

Here are examples of some typical fieldwork subjects:

- channel and flow variations within a river
- the varying pattern of land use around the centre of a settlement
- the distribution of shops within a settlement
- microclimate variations over a small area such as the school grounds
- types of environmental damage in different locations

Studying the weather

1.5 Stages of a fieldwork project

A fieldwork project will generally have four sections:

1. Introduction – aims and hypothesis

2. Methods of data collection

3. Presentation of data (results)

4. Analysis of data and conclusion

Let us look at these four stages in more detail.

Stage 1: Introduction

- Once you have chosen the subject of your fieldwork study you must come up with a hypothesis (or hypotheses, if there is more than one). This is the statement that you are going to test in your study and either accept or reject, based on the results you get. You must state your hypothesis clearly in your introduction.

  For example, you might choose to study the channel and flow variations within a river. You could test the hypothesis that: *the speed of water is faster at the outside edge of a meander than at the inside edge.* This hypothesis can then be accepted or rejected in the conclusion.

- You should make a clear statement of location. Use maps/sketches to illustrate the location of your site in Britain and locally. Label any maps and sketches carefully with a title, a key if necessary and a scale. Include in the description where you went to do the fieldwork and why the site was chosen.

- Describe the survey area and its features. Draw diagrams and include labelled photographs to describe the features.

- Link the choice of site (including its features) to information you have learnt in the classroom.

- Use secondary data, for example internet or library sources, to discuss the history of the site and any further information you may have uncovered about it.

- Ensure that the aims and objectives of the fieldwork study are clearly stated in order to be able to accept or reject the hypothesis.

Stage 2: Methods of data collection

- Having stated the hypothesis, you need to decide what methods you are going to use to test the statement. It is important that you give clear reasons why you have chosen a particular method (or methods) of data collection. You may also need to consider safety issues.

- Once you have decided upon the method or methods you are going to use, you must give a detailed description of each. This should include:
  - descriptions and labelled sketches and/or photos of the equipment used
  - a step-by-step (bullet point) guide to the process of data collection
  - a statement of whether each technique is a primary or secondary method of data collection
  - a description of any sampling techniques used (with justification as to why they were chosen).

If more than one aim is used, it is a good idea to state which hypothesis each method is trying to test. The methods you choose to collect data for your fieldwork study will depend on the chosen topic, but may include the following:

Questionnaires and surveys

A **questionnaire** is a useful tool for finding out information from an individual or a group of individuals. It is a technique that could be used to study topics such as shopping habits, use of leisure facilities, how the reduction of services in rural settlements might affect the population of villages and so on.

If using a questionnaire, you should consider the following:

- Where to conduct the survey

- Who to question:
  - a **sample** group of people, such as shoppers, or sample area, such as the town centre, needs to be decided before you create and administer your questionnaires

- The design of the questionnaire:
  - the format of the questions
  - appropriate wording
  - the number of questions

- How to conduct the survey:
  - Be polite
  - Explain that you are carrying out the survey for a school project

- Do not ask personal information such as a person's address or age (you can always estimate this without asking)
- Remember to say thank you at the end of the questionnaire

A questionnaire could be used to ask people how far they have come to use a shop and how often, on average, they visit the shop. The investigation could be widened to ask what form of transport they use to get to the shop and you may decide to estimate their age (see Fig. 1.5.1). The information collected will allow you to build up a profile of shoppers and give you plenty of scope for data analysis later in the fieldwork project.

Location: _____

Date: _____ Time: _____

Male ☐   Female ☐

Age group: Under 18 ☐   18–30 ☐   30–55 ☐   Over 55 ☐

Question 1: How far have you travelled to get to this shop?

Less than 1 mile ☐

1–5 miles ☐

5–10 miles ☐

Over 10 miles ☐

Question 2: What method of transport did you use to get to this shop?

On foot ☐

Bike ☐

Car ☐

Bus ☐

Train ☐

Other ☐   Please specify _____

Question 3: How often do you visit this shop on average?

Every day ☐

Twice a week ☐

Once a week ☐

Once a month ☐

Less than once a month ☐

Fig. 1.5.1: A well-constructed questionnaire

Surveys are similar to questionnaires but are a record of observations rather than questions asked of members of the public. These are often subjective (your own opinion). For example, an **environmental quality survey** can be used to record how litter has damaged the environment in a certain area.

Counts

This method of data collection involves recording numbers of things. For example, you could measure traffic congestion by recording the number of cars passing a certain point.

You should consider:

- the best way of recording the counts
- what you need to record (for example, the time, date and location)
- the layout of the recording sheets.

Observations

Recording what you see can be a useful skill when studying topics such as river or coastal features or land use in urban areas:

- A **field sketch** is a rough sketch of the fieldwork site and is particularly appropriate when observing natural features such as rivers and valleys. Remember to add colour and labels.

- Photographs are a useful way to record the methods and equipment used to record data.
- Maps can be used to record the location of the fieldwork and any other important features you observe.

Measurements

Measuring the subject of your study is another technique you could use. For example, you could measure the depth, width and speed of flow of a river or measure the microclimate in a local area.

When preparing to use this technique, you should consider the following:

- appropriate sampling methods
- the measurements you need to take
- the equipment you need
- the location of the instruments
- the layout of the recording sheet.

Secondary sources

In addition to your own, first-hand collection of data (called primary sources), there are a number of secondary sources that can be used for gathering information:

- The internet offers an unlimited variety of information on just about any topic. Whenever you use information from the internet, you must make reference to the website you have used. Always check the accuracy of any data you find on the internet by checking other sources and asking your teacher.
- Libraries offer a variety of books, pamphlets and CD-roms that can help you gather background information for your project.

Stage 3: Presentation of data (results)

Once the data has been collected, you must decide which data to present and how it should be presented. The findings of your research must be presented in an accurate, clear and varied manner. You may choose to use some of the following methods:

- maps
- sketches or diagrams
- tables
- graphs
- photographs – these should be annotated (labelled) (see Fig. 1.5.2).

Fig. 1.5.2: A well-annotated photo of a river survey

Maps

Maps can be used to introduce the location of the fieldwork study and can also be used in a variety of forms to present findings. It is a good idea to include a key for the symbols, a scale and a legend indicating direction.

- **Land use maps** show buildings and their uses and can also be used to describe the fieldwork area. For example, if you are researching the settlement functions of an urban area (residential, commercial, administrative, services, tourism and industrial) a land use map could be coloured and annotated to identify its location and to highlight patterns in the settlement area. A land use map can also be used to show agricultural regions (see Fig. 1.5.3).

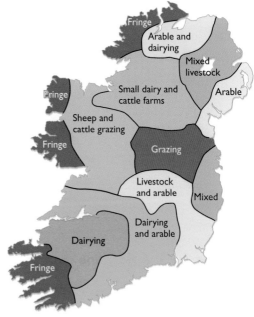

Fig. 1.5.3: A land use map showing agricultural regions in Ireland

● Like a land use map, a **choropleth map** uses colour, but it uses shades of colour to show information. Look at Fig. 1.5.4: notice how the darker shaded regions correlate to a higher score on the key. Fig. 1.5.4 only uses three shades, but you could use more to show your information clearly.

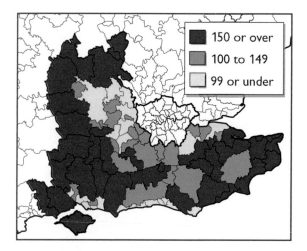

Fig 1.5.4: A choropleth map showing the numbers of play parks in electoral regions in the south of England

● A **flow map** displays movement, most often of people, from one area to another. It uses arrows of varying sizes to indicate the quantity of movement: the bigger the arrow the more movement is represented (see Fig. 1.5.5).

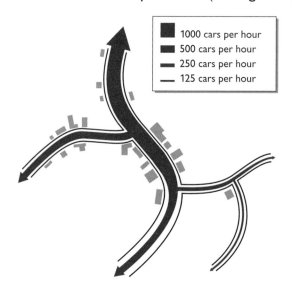

Fig 1.5.5: A flow line map showing numbers of vehicles using a route system

● A **sketch map** can be used in the introduction to your project to locate the fieldwork or later in the project as a tool for presenting data.

Sketches or diagrams

All sketches and diagrams should be clearly annotated (labelled) to explain what they are showing. Cross sections are particularly useful when displaying the width and depth of river channels. After measuring the total width of a channel with a tape measure and measuring the depth at given intervals, you can plot a graph that will show the channel shape. Look at Fig. 1.5.6: it shows a cross section measured with readings every 50 cm. The vertical axis shows the range between the maximum and minimum depths.

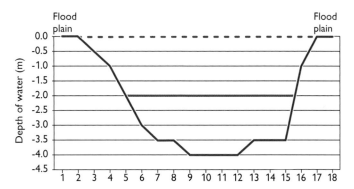

Fig 1.5.6: Cross section of a river channel

Tables

Some data can be displayed effectively in a table. Fig. 1.5.7 shows the modes of transport used by people to get to a convenience store. Data in tables is often called raw data.

Mode of transport	Number of people
On foot	11
Bike	7
Car	5
Bus	1
Train	0
Other	2

Fig. 1.5.7: Modes of transport used to get to a convenience store

Graphs

The information in a table can be processed and displayed in a graph. There are various different types of graph and you should be careful to choose the correct type for the information you are presenting. A good project will use a range of different, but appropriate, graphs to illustrate the recorded data. Graphs should have an accurate title and clear labels.

● Bar charts are probably the most basic form of presenting data.

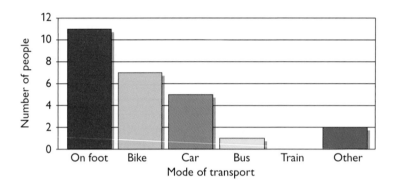

Fig. 1.5.8: A bar chart showing the modes of transport used by customers to reach a convenience store

● A pie chart illustrates data in percentage form. Once you have converted your raw data groups into percentages, allow 3.6 degrees of the protractor for each percentage point. Most computer programs used for creating charts will calculate this for you.

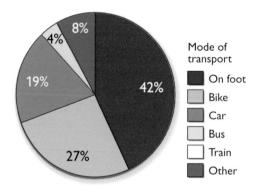

Fig. 1.5.9: A pie chart showing the modes of transport used by customers to reach a convenience store

- A pictogram uses symbols to represent the data.

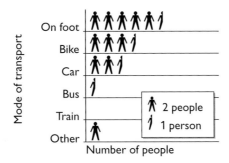

Fig. 1.5.10: A pictogram showing the modes of transport used by customers to reach a convenience store.

Other types of graph that can be used to display data are:

- line graphs – particularly suitable for showing data changing over time

- scatter graphs – help to determine whether data is following a predicted pattern, or that there is a correlation (connection) between the two sets of data

- rose diagrams – used to show wind direction.

Stage 4: Analysis of data and conclusion

The final part of any fieldwork study is to describe the patterns in the data you have presented and to use this evidence to make a judgement on the validity of the original hypothesis.

- Describe in detail what each graph or other form of data presentation shows. Quote exact figures from graphs or describe the annotated photograph or sketch. Refer, in particular to the highs, lows and general trend that the data shows.

- Make reference to the relevant geographical knowledge you have learnt in the classroom using the correct geographical terminology.

- Were the results as you had predicted? Point to evidence in the data presentation section for your answer.

- Point out any irregular or rogue results (anomalies). Explain why you think these results occurred.

- Link your results with the hypothesis you set at the beginning of the study. State clearly whether you are going to accept or reject the hypothesis based on your study.

- Describe what you have learnt from doing this study in terms of your geographical knowledge.

- Describe what you have learnt from doing this study in terms of working in groups, testing hypotheses and doing individual research.

As part of your conclusion, you should also state whether or not the data collection methods you used were a good test of the hypothesis. This is called 'evaluation'.

- Was there anything that restricted how well your chosen method worked (the limitations)?

- Were there things you planned to test but couldn't for any reason? Was the method you chose not the correct one to test the hypothesis correctly?

- What could have been done to improve the methods and to overcome any limitations?

- How did you overcome any limitations?

All this information could be used to design a new study.

Mapwork and fieldwork glossary

Bearings	Compass direction given in degress (360° in the complete circle).
Cartographers	Geographers who make maps.
Choropleth map	A map which illustrates data by colour shading increments.
Contour interval	The space between contour lines.
Contour line	A brown line on a map joining places of the same height together.
Easting	A blue grid line running up and down an OS map.
Environmental quality survey	Measures levels of environmental damage in different areas.
Field sketch	A rough drawing of the location or features studied during fieldwork.
Flow map	A map which indicates the movement of people or other variables from one area to another.
Four figure grid reference	A set of two two digit numbers indicating the grid square in which an object is located on an OS map.
Gradient	Term used to describe the steepness of a slope.
Grid square	The area of 1 kilometre square created by the grid lines on an OS map.
Hypothesis	A prediction made concerning a fieldwork aim (plural: hypotheses).
Key	A list of all the symbols used on a map and their meanings.
Landscape	The natural and human features of an area.
Land use maps	A map showing the use of each piece of land.
Northing	A blue grid line running horizontally across an OS map.
Physical features	Natural features such as rivers and hills.
Plateau	An elevated area of high land with a relatively flat surface.

Questionnaire	A form for collecting data from the public.
Relief	The shape and height of the land.
Relief features	Different landforms illustrated by the shape of the contour lines.
Ridge	A long area of elevated land with a crest.
Sample	A particular group chosen for enquiry during fieldwork.
Scale	The ratio difference between real size and actual size on a map.
Scale bar	A ruler which shows real distances on the map, usually found at the bottom of an OS map.
Scale ratio	A ratio that tells you how much bigger distances on the map are on the ground.
Six figure grid reference	A set of two three digit numbers indicating the exact location of an object on an OS map.
Sketch map	A rough hand-drawn map of an area identifying its main physical features.
Spot height	A black dot on an OS map with a number giving its height above sea level in metres.
Survey	An observation tool for recording data during fieldwork.
Triangulation pillar	Spot height surrounded by a blue triangle indicating the highest point in that area on the map.

Chapter 2: Environmental issues

In this chapter we will look at the following:

● What constitutes the environment.

● What environmental problems are being experienced on local, national and global scales.

● The stewardship of environmental issues at different scales and how this is managed.

● What specific environmental conflicts are occurring in the Peak District National Park and how these are being managed.

● What specific environmental conflicts are occurring in the Tsavo National Park in Kenya and how these are being managed.

● What is meant by sustainable development and how using renewable energy can aid sustainable development.

2.1 What is the environment and why does it need protecting?

The environment and its future

The **environment** is the term used to describe three things:

● the **landscape**

● the **atmosphere** of a given area

● the wildlife, both plants and animals, which make it their home (**habitat**).

In the world today aspects of the environment (the landscape, the atmosphere and habitats) are being threatened and, in some cases, irreversibly damaged. Unfortunately these threats and subsequent damage are frequently due to the activities of human beings (see Fig. 2.1.1). We are all responsible for preserving the environment and its resources for future generations. This concept is called **sustainable development**.

Fig. 2.1.1: A river habitat damaged by human pollution

Sustainable development at different scales

Whether an environmental problem is small, such as litter in a park, or large and more difficult, such as global warming, it needs to be managed in order to promote sustainable development. **Stewardship** is the term that describes the role of those given responsibility for managing our environment at different levels.

Local scale

We can study and care for the environment on a local scale. Caring for the local environment involves assessing what threats exist to a village, town or city and its surrounding area. The local government is required to care for the local environment by providing services such as **recycling** waste and clearing up litter, enforcing planning laws to prevent unrestricted building on **greenfield sites**, and creating preservation areas of countryside called **Country Parks** where wildlife can flourish. The local government is supported by many voluntary **conservation** groups which assist local schemes.

National scale

More widespread environmental problems on a national scale are the government's responsibility. The British government has a department called the **Environment Agency** which advises the government on the environment. It monitors **pollution** levels within our rivers and atmosphere, and can prosecute and fine offending companies. In the 1950s the government created **National Parks** (areas of natural beauty, such as Snowdonia in Wales) that it felt needed protecting from **urban sprawl** and activities that might damage the natural landscape and wildlife. Since then, the government has increased the number of National Parks in Britain to 15 and continues to preserve their landscape, wildlife and culture.

Many countries support the habitats and populations of certain animals that we term endangered. Although governments aid the protection of **endangered species**, charities such as the RSPB (Royal Society for the Protection of Birds) often take responsibility for this work.

Global scale

Some environmental issues need managing on a global scale:

- The most significant of these issues is **global warming**. Global warming can be defined as the artificial heating of our atmosphere, caused by the emission of gases such as carbon dioxide from cars, aeroplanes, industry, coal burning power stations and many other sources. These gases are referred to as greenhouse gases. As the concentration of greenhouse gases in the

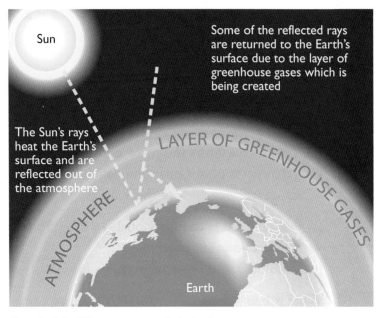

Sun

The Sun's rays heat the Earth's surface and are reflected out of the atmosphere

Some of the reflected rays are returned to the Earth's surface due to the layer of greenhouse gases which is being created

LAYER OF GREENHOUSE GASES

ATMOSPHERE

Earth

Fig. 2.1.2: The cause of global warming

Earth's atmosphere increases, more of the energy radiated outwards from the surface of the Earth is held in the atmosphere rather than escaping to space, and the global temperature rises. This increase in global temperature is causing rapid change to many environments, including an increase in **desertification** and the melting of the ice caps, leading to a rise in sea levels and possible flooding.

- Another environmental issue that needs addressing on a global scale is the preservation of environmentally unique regions such as Antarctica. Agreement between 46 different nations, including the USA, UK, China, South Africa and Australia, has seen Antarctica and its unique wildlife designated a global natural reserve under the *Protocol on Environmental Protection to the Antarctic Treaty*. This means Antarctica's land and sea resources are protected from destructive activities (see Fig. 2.1.3).

Fig. 2.1.3: Emperor penguins, in Antarctica

Exercise 2A

1. Describe exactly what is meant by the term 'the environment'.

2. Write down whether each of the following is a *local, national or global* environmental issue:

   global warming
   endangered species
   urban sprawl
   recycling

3. (a) What is meant by the term 'conservation'?
   (b) What parts of our environment need conserving and who takes responsibility for conserving each of these parts?

4. (a) Explain what is causing global warming. You may wish to draw a diagram to support your explanation.
   (b) Who do you think is responsible for global warming? Explain your answer.

5. What is being done to conserve Antarctica's fragile environment?

Extension question

6. Education is the answer to developing a society that will protect the environment rather than abuse it. Discuss various methods of educating people about the environment on a *local, national* and *global scale.*

2.2 Syllabus example: Sustainable development in the Peak District National Park

National Parks were developed in the USA as far back as the 19th century. In 1872 Yellowstone National Park was established as the world's first National Park. In a time of rapid settlement the US government decided that areas of natural beauty needed protecting. Then, as today, the US government owned most of the land within National Parks. In Britain the first National Parks were designated under the National Parks and Access to the Countryside Act 1949. British National Parks are different from those in many other countries, where they are owned and managed by the government. In England and Wales, land within a National Park is held largely in private ownership. This can lead to considerable **conflict** with the tourism industry.

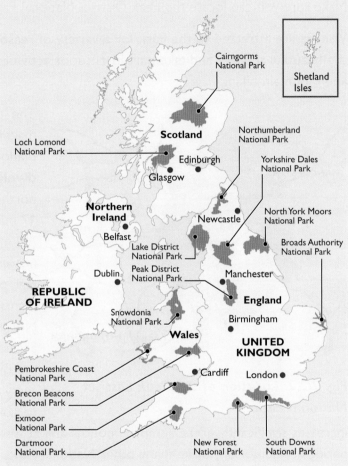

Fig 2.2.1: National Parks in Britain

The Environment Act 1995 defined the purpose of Britain's National Parks as:

1. *Conserving and enhancing the natural beauty, wildlife and cultural heritage.*

2. *Promoting opportunities for the understanding and enjoyment of their special qualities.*

The National Park Authority (NPA) must also support the economic and social wellbeing of local communities.

Attractions of the Peak District National Park

The Peak District National Park is one of Britain's most popular National Parks. Straddling the southern tip of the Pennines and covering much of Derbyshire, the Park has a varied landscape which includes limestone caves, wild moorland and rolling dales. Make sure you can locate the Peak District National Park on a blank map of Britain.

Visitors are attracted to the Park for a variety of reasons, but most come to enjoy the beautiful scenery and take part in outdoor activities such as hill walking, potholing and mountain biking.

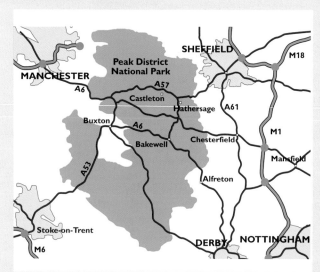

Fig. 2.2.2: Location of the Peak District National Park

The location of the Peak District makes it the most accessible National Park for many **urban dwellers** living in the Midlands and north-west of England. In fact, over 17 million people live within 95 km (60 miles) of the Park. It is the nearest large area of countryside to high population cities such as Manchester, Sheffield, Derby and Nottingham (see Fig. 2.2.2). Easy road access via the M1 and M6 motorways results in the Park carrying up to 10,000 cars on its narrow roads each day. This figure increases significantly in the summer months and at weekends and bank holidays (peak periods). Additionally, unlike many other National Parks in Britain, the Peak District National Park is well served by public transport.

Benefits of tourism

Due to its closeness to many large urban areas, the Peak District National Park receives many day trippers. However, it is estimated that over a million people each year also stay overnight in the park at hotels, bed and breakfasts, youth hostels and camping or caravan sites. This provides many locals with some income, although often only through **seasonal jobs,** which may also be part time.

Locals may also be employed in shops selling outdoor equipment or souvenirs to tourists, or promoting conservation for the National Park Authority. In all, over

£135 million is spent by tourists in the Peak District National Park each year, helping the National Park Authority to support communities such as Bakewell, a well-known **honeypot site**.

Conflicts of land use

Much of the Peak District National Park is privately owned by a number of organisations, such as the National Trust, trust estates and several water companies. There are around 2700 farmers in the Park in addition to forestry and limestone quarrying industries. Inevitably, conflicts occur between the different land users, local residents and tourist visitors. Here are two examples.

Fig. 2.2.3: Landscape of the Peak District National Park

1. Conflict between tourists and local residents

There are often mixed feelings amongst local residents in National Parks about the influence of tourist visitors. Although tourist money often provides locals with jobs, there has been an increasing trend in recent years for wealthy outsiders to buy local houses for use as holiday homes. This reduces the already limited housing available for local people, and increases house prices to levels many locals cannot afford, forcing them to move away from the area.

2. Conflict between tourists and farmers

As the Peak District National Park is an upland area, the most common type of farming is **pastoral farming**. Only about half of the farms are enclosed (crops or cattle are fenced in) with sheep grazing freely in the remaining area. Tourists threaten this method of farming by trampling pastures by walking or mountain biking off the signed footpaths.

Traditional dry stone walls – which are of cultural importance – are also damaged as people scramble over them. Gates are often left open, causing livestock to escape. Because the landscape does not necessarily look like a 'typical' farm, many tourists treat it as common land and believe they should be able to roam freely.

Environmental problems

Some landscapes and areas that are extremely beautiful and relatively easy to get to become particularly popular visitor attractions. They are often referred to as honeypot sites. These sites are encouraged because they concentrate the damage caused by tourists into a small area, thereby helping to make conservation easier in other parts of the Park. However, honeypots can suffer from overcrowding problems, littering, strain on facilities and transport networks, crime and erosion.

Fig. 2.2.4: Heavy traffic in Bakewell

Although it is well served by public transport, 95% of visitors to the Peak District National Park still arrive by car. This creates two problems:

- The narrow roads in honeypot locations can become highly congested, particularly at peak periods (see Fig. 2.2.4).

- As a result of the heavy traffic, air pollution levels in the Park during June, July and August can be higher than similar recordings taken in central London.

Fig 2.2.5: Destruction of moorland

Large numbers of walkers in a concentrated area can damage the landscape, and many of the 3000 footpaths in the park are now impassable. This leads to walkers leaving the footpaths and creating new paths, which damages the moorland vegetation that attracts tourists (see Fig. 2.2.5). Footpath erosion is made worse by the use of four-wheel drive vehicles on tracks and mountain bikes on paths.

Litter is unattractive and can lead to fires on moorland. Broken glass, parts of tin cans and plastic bags can harm or trap wildlife, particularly birds, preventing them from feeding and causing starvation. Moorland is the natural habitat for many birds that nest on the ground and are therefore easily disturbed by tourist activity.

Damage to the environment can also take the form of noise pollution and disturbance of animals.

Solutions to promote sustainable development

It is the job of the Peak District NPA to find methods to create harmony between all the different users of the Peak District National Park, and to conserve the environment from damage caused by tourism. Some of the methods that have been used include:

- Educating visitors about the issues and encouraging responsible behaviour through the use of visitor centres and information boards.

- Creating stone pathways which are more resistant to erosion can reduce the risk of footpaths wearing away. Clear signs encourage most walkers to keep to the path provided and not stray onto sensitive moorland. Providing separate mountain biking and horse riding trails helps to prevent a conflict of use and further erosion.

- Encouraging a more responsible attitude to litter disposal and persuading visitors to take their rubbish home with them.

- Employing wardens or park rangers helps to encourage Park users to stick to the pathways and take care of the environment.

- To prevent a build up of air pollution, tourists arriving by car are encouraged to use car parks on the borders of the Park and take a bus to their destination ('park and ride'). Motorists choosing to drive into the Park face heavy parking fees, especially in the honeypot towns.

- Limiting the number of houses that can be sold to tourists keeps house prices down for local residents. Such a policy also prevents a decline in public services such as post offices, local shops and petrol stations which are supported by local residents on a regular basis rather than occasionally by owners of holiday homes.

Fig. 2.2.6 summarises the problems and conflicts caused by groups in the Peak District National Park, the proposed solutions and the effects that these should have on people.

Conflict groups	Management problem	Solution	Effect on people
Tourists conflict with local residents in honeypot towns and villages by creating congestion and pollution with the additional cars.	Trying to prevent pollution and congestion with a method that will not stop visitors from coming to the Park.	Introduce park and ride schemes and charge high prices for use of local car parks.	Honeypot towns and villages have reduced congestion and pollution which will benefit locals and tourists alike. Local businesses such as shops, restaurants and hotels may not receive as much business.
Tourists conflicting with local farmers by leaving gates open and walking off footpaths, causing soil erosion.	Trying to protect the economic needs of farmers without undermining the sense of freedom that tourists come to the Park to enjoy.	Provide clearly marked signs and employ park wardens to enforce rules regarding closing gates and keeping to footpaths.	Local farmers feel that something is being done to protect their interests and will be more supportive of tourism. Tourists may feel that signposts and wardens prevent them roaming freely.
People from outside the local area conflict with locals by buying up properties in honeypot towns or villages to use as holiday homes.	Trying to ensure that local people can afford to buy property in the honeypot towns and villages and that local services are supported all year round. It is difficult to pass laws allowing only local residents to buy private properties.	Reserve a percentage of local housing for local people. Enforce a minimum occupancy period on holiday homes to ensure local services are supported.	Young people who are born in honeypot towns or villages have the opportunity to buy a house locally. Tourists are encouraged to engage with the local community if they buy holiday homes.

Fig. 2.2.6: Solutions to conflicts in areas such as the Peak District National Park

Exercise 2B

1. What is the purpose of National Parks in Britain?

2. Why does the Peak District National Park attract so many visitors? Use the following terms in your answer:
   motorways
   urban areas
   honeypots

3. (a) What is meant by the term 'conflict'?
   (b) Choose two areas of conflict between different groups of people in the Peak District National Park and explain why conflict occurs.

4. What effect do you think wealthy tourists buying houses within National Parks may have on the residents of local communities? Consider particularly the effect on community services.

5. Propose solutions to limit the following impacts of tourism and industry that occur in the Peak District National Park:
   (a) Noise and dust created from limestone quarrying.
   (b) Damage to dry stone walls by walkers scrambling over them.

   You will need to do some research to answer this question.

Extension question

6. Over 30 million people visit the Peak District National Park each year. Of these, 95% arrive by car, causing large amounts of harmful air pollution. Does the NPA need to limit the number of visitors? Consider a possible solution to this problem and discuss the advantages and disadvantages of such a scheme.

Development and indicators of development

Most countries can be broadly placed in two groups:

- Wealthy countries such as Britain, the USA and many European countries are called More Economically Developed Counties or **MEDCs**.

- Poorer countries such as Ethiopia and Bangladesh are called Less Economically Developed Countries or **LEDCs**. Kenya is an LEDC – a relatively poor country which is seeking to increase its wealth by encouraging tourists to visit and spend money.

There is a third group of countries called Newly Industrialised Countries or **NICs**, which are becoming wealthier due to the rapid growth of their manufacturing sector. China is an excellent example of an NIC. It cannot be classified as an MEDC because only a very small percentage of its population enjoys the wealth and benefits of China's global dominance of manufacturing.

Poorer countries naturally try to increase their wealth in order to enjoy the benefits of a higher **standard of living**. Kenya and other LEDCs such Egypt, Thailand and India have tried to do this by encouraging the growth of tourism. They are hoping to follow the examples of countries such as Greece, Spain and Italy, which were relatively poor in the mid-20th century but are now prosperous MEDCs, partly as a result of tourism. The wealth and standard of living of a country's population can be measured in a number of ways; these are called **indicators of development**:

- Gross Domestic Product (**GDP**) is defined as the total value of all goods and services produced within a country in one year.

- The total amount of money a country makes, plus the money it makes from foreign investments, is called the Gross National Product or **GNP**. GNP gives us an indication of how economically developed a country is, but it does not measure the standard of living experienced by a country's people.

- The Human Development Index (**HDI**) combines indicators of adult literacy rates, life expectancy and income to give a more balanced view of the level of **development**. Countries are given an HDI score between 0 and 1. A score nearer to 1 indicates a more developed country. For example, the HDI for the UK was 0.849 in 2010, whereas Niger's HDI was 0.261. Fig. 2.3.1 shows how the HDI varies around the world.

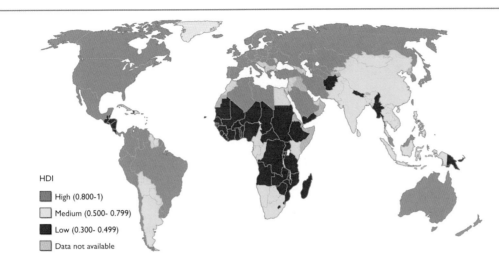

Fig. 2.3.1: World map showing the Human Development Index (HDI), 2010

2.3 Extra example: Sustainable development in Tsavo National Park in Kenya

Attractions of Kenya and the Tsavo National Park

Kenya has many physical advantages that make it very attractive to tourists. These are illustrated in Fig. 2.3.3 (page 62):

- It has large areas of **savannah** grassland, the habitat for wildlife such as elephants, rhinos, buffalo, lions and leopards, the 'Big Five' that tourists come to see on **safaris**.

- The beautiful Great Rift Valley overlooked by Mount Kenya provides a challenging environment for walkers and mountain climbers (see Fig. 2.3.2).

- Sandy beaches which line the Indian Ocean coastline attract tourists in search of relaxing holidays.

- Kenya's coastline has the added attraction of coral reefs which tourists may also choose to visit for scuba diving or snorkelling holidays.

- Tourists often prefer Kenya to other destinations as it offers many different activities as well as a pleasant climate.

Fig. 2.3.2: Great Rift Valley landscape, Kenya

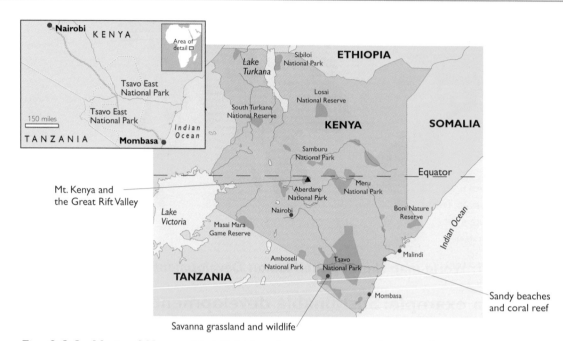

Fig. 2.3.3: Map of Kenya highlighting its advantages for tourism

A distinct advantage for Kenya's economy is the fact that Kenya attracts tourists throughout the year. Fig. 2.3.3 illustrates that Kenya is on the Equator, ensuring that it experiences sunny and consistently hot weather throughout the year. For this reason it is a particularly popular destination for European tourists in the winter months.

A principal tourist attraction in Kenya is the Tsavo National Park, a major wildlife reserve. The park covers an area bigger than Wales (21,812 sq km/8422 sq miles) and is split in two by the main road between Nairobi and Mombasa (Fig. 2.3.3) to create Tsavo East and Tsavo West:

Fig. 2.3.4: Elephants in Tsavo East

- Tsavo East is mostly flat semi-arid plains which support a variety of wildlife including the 'Big Five' as well as less well-known species such as the blue monkey, the African civet and the white-tailed mongoose. In Tsavo East is the Mudanda Rock, a large permeable rock formation that attracts a lot of the region's rainfall and provides drinking grounds for the large elephant population.

- Tsavo West is more mountainous and wetter than Tsavo East and has a varied landscape that includes swamps, lakes and areas of savannah grassland which support the black rhino. Mizima Springs is a wetland area that has been adapted so that tourists can view hippos in their natural habitat through giant plate glass windows.

Although the Tsavo National Park is mainly renowned for its great elephant herds (see Fig. 2.3.4), the network of roads and paths that cover over 800 km (500 miles) in the Park allows tourists to see a wide variety of animals, including reptiles such as the crocodile and the black-necked cobra. The vegetation of the Park also provides the habitat for over 500 species of bird, including ostriches, herons, kestrels and kingfishers.

Benefits of tourism

The Kenyan authorities have permitted only one safari lodge within the Park itself in order to minimise the negative effects of tourism. However, several lodges have been built on the borders of the Park. These lodges provide employment for locals as guides for game viewing, walking safaris or bird watching. Because Tsavo is so close to the Indian Ocean, it attracts visitors from the coast. Therefore, many hotels have been built, which provide jobs for nearly 200,000 Kenyans. These are permanent, not seasonal, jobs. All hotels charge a tourist tax which the government puts towards developing Kenya's **infrastructure** (new schools, roads, hospitals, etc). Annually Kenya receives approximately 780,000 tourist visitors, generating over £300 million for the economy.

Conflicts of land use

The development of tourism to boost Kenya's economy has, however, created several conflicts of land use between local people and developers:

- Increased tourist numbers and additional safari vehicles crossing the dry soil, in order to get closer to the wildlife, have increased the level of **soil erosion** in the Tsavo National Park. Soil erosion damages vegetation and threatens the habitat supporting the wild animals that tourists have come to see.

- Many local communities that used to live along the Indian Ocean coast have been forced to leave their homes (**forced migration**) to make way for hotel developments.

Environmental problems

As well as the problems listed above, irresponsible tourists have further damaged the environment by touching and walking on coral reefs. Many people also consider the hotels built on the Indian Ocean coast to be **visual pollution**.

Social problems

The Kenyan government has a policy that one-quarter of income from tourist sites should benefit the local economy. However, difficulties at central and local government level have meant that this does not happen. Additionally, a large proportion of hotels in Kenya are in fact owned by **multi-national corporations**, such as Hilton or Hyatt-Regency, which are owned by American or European companies. Over 90% of the profits leave the country, so money is rarely re-invested in the local infrastructure by such companies.

Although tourism creates permanent jobs in Tsavo National Park and other areas, the better-paid jobs such as hotel managers, childcare supervisors and water sports instructors are rarely awarded to local people.

Violent crime rates have soared in Kenya which is starting to have a significant impact on the number of tourists choosing it as a holiday destination.

Solutions to promote sustainable development

It is the job of the Kenyan government and Tsavo National Park Authority to find methods of creating harmony between the different land users in Tsavo National Park and conserve the environment from damage caused by the impact of tourism.

To reduce the impact of soil erosion and other environmental threats from tourism, park wardens in Tsavo National Park enforce a strict code of conduct for visitors (see Fig. 2.3.5).

- It is forbidden to travel in an open vehicle while in the Park.

- Stay in your vehicle all the time. Get out only at designated areas.

- Off-road driving is not allowed. View the wildlife from a distance with binoculars.

- Off-road driving destroys vegetation, might kill wildlife and could interfere with the daily routine of animals. The tracks formed become an eyesore.

- Animals have a right of way. Do not harass them or make loud sounds – this might scare them and make them nervous. Patience pays!

- Remember not to litter.

- Remember: do not take anything but photographs and leave nothing but footprints.

Fig. 2.3.5: Code of conduct for visitors to Tsavo National Park

To overcome the environmental problems caused by the rapid development of the Indian Ocean coast, the Kenyan government has now restricted development, and created a National Maritime Park along the coast north of Mombasa.

To deal with the number of multi-national chains of hotels and the fact that local people are rarely given the better paid jobs, the Kenyan government promotes Kenyan-owned hotels.

In order to reduce crime, the Kenyan government has invested some of the income generated from tourism in strengthening its police force, and has increased criminal penalties.

Fig. 2.3.6 summarises the problems caused by conflict groups in the Tsavo National Park, the proposed solutions and the effects that these should have on people.

Areas of conflict	Management problem	Solution	Effect on people
Tourists in jeeps on safari cause soil erosion.	Trying to balance the need to prevent irreversible environment damage with the reliance of many locals on tourism. Encouraging tourism without exploiting or damaging the traditional way of life of tribespeople.	Limit size, frequency and routes of safari vehicles in order to reduce impact and prevent unneccessary soil erosion.	Tribes people living on the savannah have a better chance of maintaining their nomadic way of life. Local people running safaris may have a reduced income by limiting safari numbers.
Habitat destruction and deforestation caused by promoting hotel development.	As above. As above.	Strict limitations on lodge development in national parks. Tsavo has only one lodge, although several have been created on its borders.	The savannah, which is so important to the nomadic way of life of local tribespeople, is protected from development. Tourists may choose another country to take a safari due to limited accommodation options in Kenya's national parks.
Developers force locals off their land in order to make way for tourist accommodation.	Balancing tourism in a sustainable manner while trying to protect the traditional lifestyles of local communities.	Encourage developers to employ locals at their hotel developments. Protect land by creating national parks and marine reserves.	Local people have an income from a tourist industry job, e.g. a waiter. The cultural traditions of local people can be lost as they adopt a more westernised lifestyle.

Fig. 2.3.6: Solutions to conflicts in Tsavo National Park

Exercise 2C

1. (a) Explain what is meant by the terms MEDC and LEDC.
    (b) Name five MEDCs and five LEDCs.

2. (a) Describe the geographical advantages that attract tourists to Kenya.
    (b) What is seasonal employment? Why are tourism jobs in Kenya not seasonal?

3. Imagine that you have just spent a day on safari in Tsavo National Park. Give an account of the landscape and wildlife you have experienced.

4. Draw a spider diagram with the words 'benefits of tourism for local people' written in the middle. Think of the advantages that tourism brings to the people of Kenya and add them as legs to your spider diagram. If you have time, illustrate each leg with a sketch.

5. (a) Describe one way in which tourism has damaged the environment in Kenya and provide possible solutions to overcome this damage.
   (b) Describe one way in which tourism has had a negative impact upon the people of Kenya and provide possible solutions to these negative impacts.

Extension question

6. In a report written by Mike Crawley (a freelance writer based in East Africa), the Dean of the Faculty of Forestry Resources and Wildlife Management at Moi University, Kenya, Professor Baraza Wangila, warns that 'Kenya's wildlife could become a victim of its own success at attracting tourists'. Discuss what you think is meant by this statement.

2.4 Extension topic: Sustainable development

The concept of sustainable development

As we have seen, sustainable development is the idea of protecting our planet's environment and resources for future generations. Since the **Industrial Revolution** human beings have been extracting **fossil fuels** to supply our ever-growing demand for energy. This increase in demand has led to major environmental problems such as pollution, deforestation and global warming. Only relatively recently has the international community begun to address sustainable development to some degree at local, national and global levels. In 1992 world leaders met in Rio de Janeiro in Brazil for an Earth Summit and created two main policies to promote sustainable development: *The Rio Declaration on Environment and Development* and *Agenda 21*.

The Rio Declaration on Environment and Development set out 27 different principles to which the international community should adhere. For example, Principle 23, below, was created to encourage member countries of the **United Nations** to protect the environment in countries where the local people were unable to practise sustainable development for themselves.

Agenda 21 set out methods in which sustainable development could be achieved at national and local levels but recognised that LEDCs and poorer countries were at a disadvantage, and would need to be assisted in their efforts towards these methods.

> **Principle 23**
>
> The environment and natural resources of people under oppression, domination and occupation shall be protected.

Examples of sustainable development in MEDCs and LEDCs

MEDCs

Kirklees is a region in West Yorkshire with a high **population density**. It is sandwiched between Manchester to the west, Bradford and Leeds to the north and the Peak District National Park to the south (Fig. 2.4.1). In response to the proposals of *Agenda 21* aimed at the local scale, Kirklees Metropolitan Council has come up with a plan for reducing transport problems and their impact upon the environment. Four travel-based targets

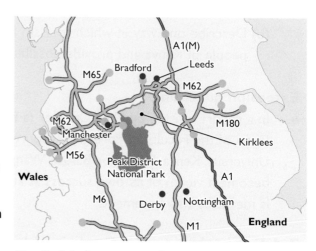

Fig. 2.4.1: Location of Kirklees

have been identified by the council. Fig. 2.4.2 shows each specific target, the aim of the target and the method by which the target may be achieved.

Target	Aim	Method
1. To increase the number of people working from home.	To reduce the use of cars and resulting congestion/pollution, particularly at rush hour times.	Investing in information technology (IT) and promoting flexible working hours within local businesses.
2. To increase the number of residents working in Kirklees.	To prevent people using their cars to commute out of Kirklees.	Providing grants to encourage businesses to locate in Kirklees rather than elsewhere in the region.
3. To reduce congestion.	To reduce the pollution and related problems caused by congestion.	Possible schemes include building bypasses, charging high rates for town centre parking and allowing cars which have more than one occupant to use bus lanes or the hard shoulder of motorways (e.g. M62).
4. To increase the use of public transport.	To reduce congestion and pollution.	Invest in railways, bus services, and possible tram networks for larger settlements.

Fig. 2.4.2: Kirklees Metropolitan Council travel-based targets

Fig 2.4.3: Indonesia

LEDCs

Look at the map of the islands that make up Indonesia (Fig. 2.4.3) and in particular the islands of Java and Bali. Indonesia is an LEDC with a population of over 200 million people and total land area of 1.9 million sq km (734,000 sq miles) resulting in a high population density. Around 44.3% of the 95 million-strong workforce is employed in **agriculture**. As is the case in most LEDCs, Indonesia is experiencing high population growth, resulting in more pressure on the land (such as **deforestation**) to meet the needs of the population.

Fig. 2.4.4: A commercial rubber plantation in Indonesia

Fig. 2.4.5: Women winnowing rice grains in a paddy field in Bali, Indonesia

The Indonesian island of Java practises **monoculture** of crops such as sugar, rubber (see Fig. 2.4.4) and coffee which are grown for sale on the global market. These monocultures have grown as the global price of the commodities has reduced and Java's population has increased. This has led to serious soil erosion and nutrient depletion, as well as water pollution from pesticides.

However, the authorities in Java are studying the neighbouring Indonesian island of Bali (see Fig. 2.4.5) as an example of how to practise agriculture in a sustainable way. Since the Rio Earth Summit of 1992, Bali has developed sustainable methods of farming, such as crop rotation which allows the soil to regain nutrients. In addition, farmers are encouraged to use alternatives to pesticides which limit environmental pollution.

Renewable and non-renewable resources

Think about the demand you have made for energy today. From the moment you got up and switched on your bedroom light you have more than likely been using electricity to provide energy for all sorts of appliances. We can divide the resources that create energy into two simple groups: **renewable resources** and **non-renewable resources** (see Fig. 2.4.6).

Renewable resources
- Will never run out
- Do not pollute the environment
- Only work in specific locations
- Can be destructive to the environment
- Are expensive to concentrate

Include
- Solar
- Geothermal
- Hydroelectric power (HEP)
- Wind
- Tidal

Non-renewable resources
- Are produced by systems that are already in place
- Are cheap to maintain
- Will run out in the future
- Pollute the environment

Include
- Coal
- Oil
- Natural gas
- Nuclear

Fig. 2.4.6: Renewable and non-renewable resources

Non-renewable resources include the **raw materials** of three main fossil fuels (oil, coal and natural gas) as well as **nuclear power**. They are non-renewable because they are sources of power that have taken millions of years to form and cannot be replaced once they are used. It has been predicted that all fossil fuels will run out within the next 200 years assuming nothing is done to find new reserves or develop any new processing technologies. Fossil fuels pollute the environment when burnt in power stations or used in car engines. As we have already learnt, global warming and its associated problems have been caused by a greater concentration of greenhouse gases in the Earth's atmosphere.

Nuclear energy is produced by splitting or fusing the nuclei of atoms; uranium is a material frequently used in this process. The advantages of nuclear energy are that a small amount of raw material produces a large amount of energy and doesn't give off atmospheric pollutants. The raw materials are relatively cheap. The disadvantages are that the radioactive waste from nuclear power plants has to be encased in iron and concrete and buried below the ocean surface to minimise damage to the environment. Accidental leakage of nuclear materials can have a devasting impact.

Alternative energy is made from renewable resources such as **HEP**, solar and wind power will never run out. However, they tend to be expensive to install and maintain and it is costly to concentrate the energy extracted. They are usually landscape/location specific:

Fig. 2.4.7: Wind farm in Cornwall

- Geothermal energy can only be made use of in tectonically active areas such as Iceland or New Zealand.

- Wind turbines need to be located in areas that receive a continuous **prevailing wind** such as the west coast of Britain (see Fig. 2.4.7).

- HEP dams must be in highland areas to create a suitable dam wall and reservoir.

Destruction of the environment can also be caused when valleys are flooded and tidal barriers and wind farms are erected. However, many renewable resource technologies are still being researched although they may never provide sufficient energy on a national or global scale.

Since the Industrial Revolution, MEDCs have relied on fossil fuels to power industry and supply their demands for energy. More recently nuclear power has also provided a significant amount of energy in MEDCs along with an increasing input from renewable resources, particularly HEP. In France, for example, nuclear power stations now account for 78% of energy production (according to the EIA International Energy Annual 2005). Because LEDCs are limited by both their landscape/location and their wealth, these countries typically still rely on fossil fuels.

Fig. 2.4.8: Dinorwig HEP station in North Wales

Fig. 2.4.9: Upper reservoir at Dinorwig, North Wales

Dinorwig HEP station in North Wales

One of the British government's earliest attempts to provide a sustainable regional energy resource by harnessing water power was the construction of the HEP station at Dinorwig in North Wales (see Fig. 2.4.8). The power station was built into the mountainside on the edge of Llyn (lake) Peris in 1984. A reservoir was created further up the mountain (see Fig. 2.4.9) from which water flows with great force down the slope, powering the six large turbines. During off-peak electricity periods (when demand for electricity is much lower) the water is then pumped back up to the higher reservoir.

Other HEP stations are built near fast-flowing rivers in highland areas (see Fig. 2.4.10). A high dam wall is built to bridge the valley and the area behind the dam wall will then be flooded to create a reservoir. This can be used to supply fresh water to the local and neighbouring regions, as well as being used for tourist and leisure activities such as fishing, waterskiing and sailing. Building dams and reservoirs on upland rivers also allows the authorities to control the flow of water into the flood plain, thereby reducing the possibility of flooding in winter months.

The disadvantage of such HEP schemes is the cost, not only of building and maintaining the dam wall, but also of buying the land that will form the reservoir. In addition, there may be environmental impact on river wildlife.

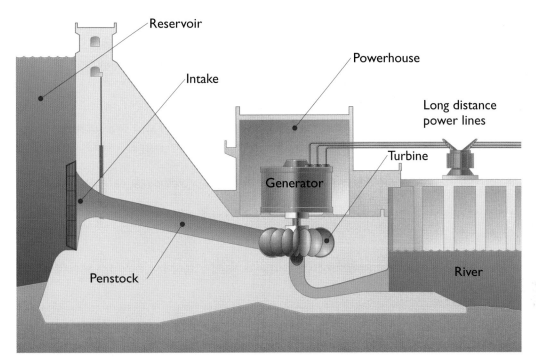

Fig. 2.4.10: A typical layout of a hydroelectric power station

Exercise 2D

1. (a) What is sustainable development?
    (b) What can be done on a local scale to aid sustainable development? Refer to examples in your local community if you can.

2. Draw a spider diagram to show how Kirklees Metropolitan Council has responded to the proposal of *Agenda 21*.

3. Create a flow chart to illustrate the demands for energy that you make in a typical day.

4. (a) Write sentences to define the following terms:
    renewable resources
    non-renewable resources
    fossil fuels

    (b) Why is it a good idea to replace non-renewable energy resources with renewable resources?

5. How can energy be generated from water? Refer to the Dinorwig power station example. You may wish to draw a diagram to help your explanation.

Extension question

6. Referring to examples in MEDCs and LEDCs, explain why sustainable development needs to be adopted on local, national and global scales.

End of chapter activity

The environment is a good topic to debate. Choose a chairman and speakers to debate any of the following motions:

All visitors to National Parks should be charged for entry with or without a car.

The government has no right to penalise individuals for having vehicles that produce a lot of carbon dioxide.

The land from which locals have been evicted to make way for tourism in Kenya should be returned to them immediately.

Glossary

Agriculture	Farming.
Alternative energy	Energy that is made from renewable resources such as solar power, HEP and geothermal energy.
Atmosphere	The mass of gases surrounding the earth.
Conflict	A disagreement between two or more people (or groups of people). For example, land use conflict between tourists and farmers in National Parks.
Conservation	The protection, preservation or restoration of the environment.
Country Parks	Areas of countryside that are protected from development.
Deforestation	The cutting down and clearing of forested areas which often leads to soil erosion and other environmental consequences.
Desertification	The process by which areas of desert are created by the destruction of natural vegetation.
Development	How rich or poor a country is in comparison with other countries. Measured by indicators such as GNP, health standards, life expectancy, etc. (See LEDC and MEDC.)
Endangered species	Animals, insects or plants which are at risk of becoming extinct.
Environment	The physical setting where humans, plants and animals live amongst each other (the landscape, the atmosphere and the habitat).
Environment Agency	Government department charged with protecting the environment.
Forced migration	The movement of people against their will.
Fossil fuels	Non-renewable power resources, for example: coal, oil and natural gas.

GDP	Gross Domestic Product is one of the ways of measuring the size of a country's economy. The GDP of a country is defined as the total value of all goods and services produced within the country in a given period of time (usually a calendar year).
Global warming	Rapid heating of the earth's atmosphere caused by the build-up of greenhouse gases such as carbon dioxide.
GNP	Gross National Product is the GDP of a country plus the income earned from foreign investments. (See GDP.)
Greenfield site	Land on the outskirts of a city that has not been built on.
Habitat	The natural environment of plants and animals.
HDI	Human Development Index is a measure which combines indicators of life expectancy, literacy, education and income for countries worldwide.
HEP	Hydroelectric power – energy created by harnessing the power of fast moving water from a dam using turbines.
Honeypot site	A town, village or attraction in a National Park which is very popular with tourists.
Indicators of development	Measures of how developed a country is, such as GNP and HDI.
Industrial Revolution	A period of history when the invention and use of steam-powered machines led to a massive increase in the number of factories. As most factories were located in towns and cities, people left the countryside to work in them. This first began in Britain between the late 18th and early 19th centuries before spreading to the rest of the world.
Infrastructure	The network of basic services such as schools, roads, hospitals, etc.
Landscape	The natural and human features of an area.
LEDC	Less Economically Developed Country.
MEDC	More Economically Developed Country.
Monoculture	Growing just one crop in a field year after year.

Multi-national corporations	Businesses that have offices or factories in several countries.
National Park	An area of beautiful countryside that has been designated by law to have its natural beauty and heritage conserved, and to promote its enjoyment to the public.
NIC	Newly Industrialised Countries are those countries whose economies are undergoing rapid economic growth, outpacing other developing countries, but that have not yet reached MEDC status.
Non-renewable resource	A resource such as coal, oil, natural gas or nuclear power (uranium) that can only be used once and will therefore at some stage run out.
Nuclear power	Energy produced by nuclear reactors.
Pastoral farming	Rearing animals.
Pollution	Contamination of the environment by gases, noise, litter or waste produced by individuals or industry.
Population density	A measurement of population living in a particular area.
Prevailing wind	A wind from the predominant, or most usual, direction. The prevailing wind in Britain is from the south-west, blowing on average seven days out of ten from this direction.
Raw materials	Natural resources taken from the ground or sea which are used to manufacture items or power.
Recycling	Collecting waste materials and making use of them again.
Renewable resource	A resource is said to be renewable if it can be used again and again, such as solar power, HEP and geothermal energy. These resources tend to be expensive to set up, but do not pollute the environment as do non-renewable resources.
Safari	A guided tour in search of wild animals.
Savannah	Grassland, lying between the equatorial rain forests and the hot desert regions, which forms the habitat for many African animals.

Seasonal jobs	Jobs that only last a few months because they rely on activities (usually tourist activities) during a particular season (e.g. the summer months or ski season).
Soil erosion	The removal of soil by wind or water, often initiated by deforestation.
Standard of living	The level of services people living in a country experience, such as health, education, electricity and running water.
Stewardship	The management and caring for a place or area by a charity, private body or government.
Sustainable development	A concept expressing the need for people and governments to manage responsibly the world's resources and environment for future generations.
United Nations	The United Nations (UN), with its headquarters in New York, is an international organisation the aims of which are to enourage cooperation in international law, international security, economic development, social progress and human rights issues across the world.
Urban dwellers	People living in urban areas.
Urban sprawl	The continued outward growth of cities into the surrounding countryside which can be sometimes restricted by the green belt.
Visual pollution	Visual pollution is the term given to items such as unsightly buildings, spoil tips or heavy industrial complexes spoiling the beauty of a natural landscape.

Chapter 3: Tectonic processes

In this chapter we will look at:

- How the Earth's crust is broken into different types of tectonic plates.

- What type of tectonic activity occurs at the plate boundaries.

- What can happen during earthquakes and volcanic events and the consequences in the following weeks and months.

- How the level of development of a country affects how it copes with an earthquake or volcanic event.

- What can be done to predict and prepare for earthquakes and volcanic events.

3.1 Where do earthquakes and volcanoes occur?

The Earth's structure

Ever since the Earth's formation (an estimated 4,600,000,000 – four thousand six hundred million years ago) it has been slowly cooling down. This has led to the formation of a **crust**, a thin solid layer of rock that forms the surface of our planet (Fig. 3.1.1). Below the crust is the **mantle**, which is made of semi-solid rock and has properties of both a liquid and a solid, and can therefore break and flow. At the very centre of the Earth is a **core**, which is believed to be a solid surrounded by liquid metals that reach temperatures of over 5000 °C!

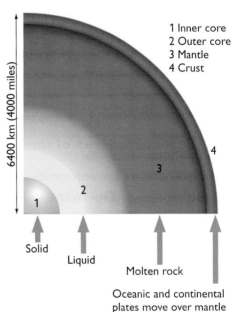

1 Inner core
2 Outer core
3 Mantle
4 Crust

6400 km (4000 miles)

Solid
Liquid
Molten rock
Oceanic and continental plates move over mantle

Fig. 3.1.1: The Earth's structure

Oceanic and continental tectonic plates

The Earth's crust is not one seamless layer, but it is broken up into many different sections of varying sizes called **tectonic plates**. These huge sections of the Earth's surface rest upon the deep semi-solid layer of the mantle beneath them. The edges where the plates meet are called **plate boundaries**. Nearly all **earthquakes** and **volcanoes** occur at these boundaries.

Fig. 3.1.2 shows a simplified map of how the Earth's crust is split into tectonic plates. (The map also shows the five volcanoes you need to know for the Location Knowledge section of the Common Entrance exam, and the earthquake and volcano examples covered in this chapter.)

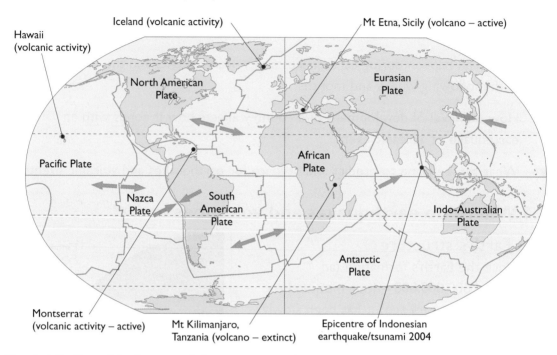

Fig. 3.1.2: Simplified map of the tectonic plates

Active volcanoes are volcanoes that have erupted in the last 2000 years and are likely to erupt again. **Dormant volcanoes** are volcanoes that have erupted in the last 2000 years but not in the last 200 years. An **extinct volcano** is a volcano that has not erupted in the last 2000 years and will not erupt again.

There are two types of tectonic plates:

- **Oceanic plates** that line our ocean floors are thinner, newer and made of more dense rock than continental plates

- **Continental plates** that make up the continental landmasses we live on are thicker, older and made of less dense rock than oceanic plates.

These tectonic plates move as heat rises and falls inside the mantle, creating **convection currents** (see Fig. 3.1.3).

Try to identify the oceanic and continental plates in Fig. 3.1.2.

Plate boundaries

The point where tectonic plates meet is called a plate boundary. What happens at these boundaries depends on the type of tectonic plates found there and the direction in which they are being pushed by the convection currents in the mantle below. Heat from the Earth's core causes rising hot convection currents within the mantle. The plates 'float' on the hot semi-solid mantle beneath and their movement is caused by these convection currents (see Fig. 3.1.3).

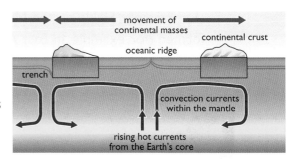

Fig. 3.1.3: Formation and action of convection currents

There are four types of plate boundary: constructive, destructive, collision and conservative or sliding.

Constructive plate boundary

Constructive plate boundaries occur when the plates move apart. This can happen either between two oceanic plates or two continental plates (see Fig. 3.1.4).

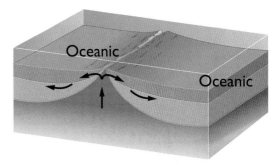

Fig. 3.1.4: Constructive plate boundary between oceanic plates

- When two oceanic plates move apart, **magma** rises to the sea floor and creates undersea volcanoes. Because the **lava** is under pressure from the ocean above and is not rich in dissolved gases, eruptions tend to be of a constant nature and not very violent.

A new ocean floor is created at constructive plate boundaries, a process often referred to as sea floor spreading. A good example of a constructive plate boundary is the Mid-Atlantic Ridge which forms the boundary between the Eurasian plate and the North American plate. Identify this on Fig. 3.1.2 (page 80). Iceland is located on the Mid-Atlantic Ridge and was created by an undersea volcano piercing the ocean surface. More recently, in 1963, a smaller island off the coast of Iceland, called Surtsey, was created in this way.

Mount Surtsey eruption in Iceland

- When two continental plates move apart, gentle volcanic eruptions take place (for example, Hekla on the Mid-Atlantic Ridge in Iceland), or rift valleys are formed (for example, in East Africa). Iceland grows in width by about 4 cm (1.6 inches) each year as the Eurasian and North American plates move apart and magma flows into the gap, creating new crust (see Fig. 3.1.5).

Fig. 3.1.5: Thingvellir, Iceland – mid-Atlantic rift valley between the Eurasian and North American plates

Destructive plate boundary

At **destructive plate boundaries** the plates move towards each other. This happens between a continental plate and an oceanic plate (see Fig. 3.1.6).

Where an oceanic plate moves towards a continental plate, the denser oceanic plate slides underneath the continental plate,

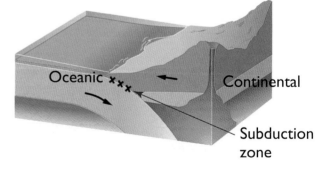

Fig. 3.1.6: Destructive plate boundary

often creating an oceanic trench. As it slides down into the mantle, considerable friction occurs in the **subduction zone**, the area where the oceanic plate slides beneath the continental plate, causing earthquakes or volcanoes.

(If the subduction zone is some distance from the coast, large earthquakes can cause **tsunamis**.) The oceanic plate is absorbed into the mantle, building pressure which is periodically released through the crust as a volcanic eruption. Volcanic eruptions at destructive plate boundaries tend to be violent because seawater and marine life from the ocean floor are taken down into the mantle and turned into hydrogen and nitrogen. These gases mix with the pressurised magma in the mantle and lead to large and spectacular eruptions. On the west coast of the South American continent, the Andes mountains contain several active volcanoes, including Sabancaya. This area experiences a high frequency of earthquakes due to the oceanic Nazca plate sliding underneath the continental South American plate.

Collision plate boundary

A **collision boundary** is found where two continental plates meet (see Fig. 3.1.7). Because both plates are the same thickness and density, neither will slide beneath the other, and both are forced upwards, creating high mountain ranges sometimes referred to as fold mountains. This collision causes frequent earthquakes but, because

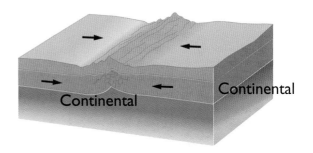

Fig. 3.1.7: Collision boundary

the crust is very thick at collision boundaries and pressure is not created in the mantle, volcanic activity does not occur.

The Himalayan Mountains have been created where the Indian and Eurasian plates are in collision (see Fig. 3.1.8). The Indo-Australian plate is still moving at a rate of 67 mm (2.6 inches) a year (over the next 10 million years it will travel about 1500 km (932 miles) into Asia). This causes the Himalayas to rise by about 5 mm (0.2 inches) a year, making them geologically active. The movement of the Indian plate causes occasional earthquakes, making this region seismically active. (Seismic means relating to vibrations of the Earth's crust caused by earthquakes and plate movement.)

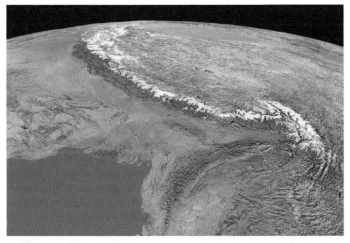

Fig. 3.1.8: Satellite image of the Himalayas

Conservative or sliding plate boundary

At a **conservative** or **sliding plate boundary** two plates, either oceanic or continental, slide past each other and crust is neither created nor destroyed (see Fig. 3.1.9). The friction between the plates sliding past each other builds up and when the stress is too much for the

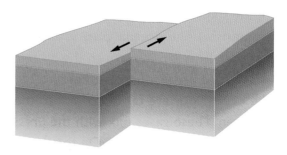

Fig. 3.1.9: Conservative or sliding plate boundary

rocks to absorb, the built up energy is released. This release of energy causes fractures of the Earth's crust and sometimes causes earthquakes. Volcanic activity does not occur at conservative plate boundaries. Periodically, the plates **lock** together at a certain point and pressure builds up over a number of years. Eventually the lock breaks and the plates jolt past each other, creating large and often devastating earthquakes.

Fig. 3.1.10: San Andreas Fault, California

An example of a fracture associated with this type of plate boundary is the San Andreas Fault on the western coast of North America (see Fig. 3.2.10). This is one part of a highly complex system of faults where the Pacific and North American plates move relative to each other, the rate of slippage averaging approximately 33–37 mm (1.3–1.5 inches) a year. This **fault** line has caused several severe earthquakes in populated areas along the west coast of the USA including San Francisco, Loma Prieta (in 1989) and Parkfield (in 2004).

Fig. 3.1.11: Damage caused by the Northridge earthquake in 1994

Exercise 3A

1. Earthquakes and volcanoes occur at particular locations around the world. Explain why, using examples.

2. What is the difference between an oceanic and a continental plate? Explain how this difference affects what happens when oceanic and continental plates meet.

3. (a) Explain what happens at a destructive plate boundary, using the following terms:

    mantle
    friction
    subduction zone
    pressure
    oceanic plate
    continental plate

    (b) Name an example of a destructive plate boundary.

4. The Himalayan Mountains are the highest mountains in the world. Explain why these are often called *fold* mountains.

5. (a) Draw a labelled diagram to illustrate what happens at a conservative or sliding plate boundary.

    (b) Why do volcanoes not occur at conservative or collision plate boundaries?

Extension question

6. Explain why volcanoes at destructive plate boundaries are more explosive than those at constructive plate boundaries. Use examples to illustrate your answer.

3.2 Syllabus example: Earthquake in an LEDC, Indonesia 2004

On 26th December 2004, the third largest earthquake ever recorded, measuring 9.3 on the **Richter scale** (a measure of the amount of energy released by an earthquake), occurred under the sea just off the coast of the Indonesian Island of Sumatra (see Fig. 3.1.2, page 80). The earthquake itself caused considerable damage on land, particularly in Banda Aceh, the nearest city to the **epicentre** (the point on the Earth's surface directly above where the earthquake originated), and was felt as far away as India. But far greater damage was caused by the resulting tsunami, triggered by the undersea earthquake, as it spread across the entire Indian Ocean killing over 275,000 people. The Indian Ocean tsunami was one of the worst natural disasters in recorded history.

Causes

Indonesia experiences earthquakes and volcanoes due to its location on a destructive plate boundary. The earthquake in 2004 was caused by the action of the oceanic Indo-Australian plate sliding underneath the continental Eurasian plate and the subsequent large amount of pressure built up in the subduction zone (see Fig. 3.2.1). Just before 8 o'clock in the morning, Indonesian time, this pressure was released as the Indo-Australian plate jolted further down towards the mantle, forcing the Eurasian plate to rise up a massive 15 metres (49 feet).

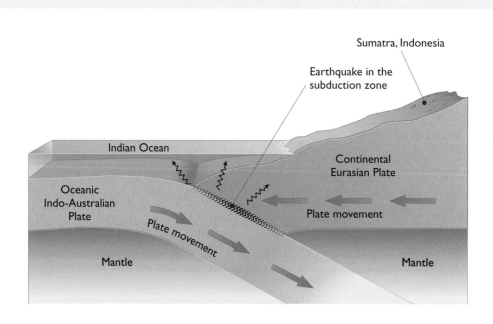

Fig. 3.2.1: Plate movement causing the Indonesian earthquake in 2004

Effects

The effects of a natural disaster such as the Indonesian earthquake and tsunami can be broadly split into two groups: the immediate effects and the longer term consequences.

Many of the effects can also fall into two or all three of the following groups:

- Environmental effects – the way in which the landscape is damaged by the event, such as the tsunami flooding coastal land.

- Economic effects – the way in which property, transport and industry are affected and the cost of rebuilding this infrastructure.

- Social effects – the ways in which people suffer injury, death and the destruction of their homes and family network.

Immediate effects

- The earthquake caused the land to shake violently for up to 10 minutes, causing significant damage to buildings in Sumatra, particularly in the capital city of Banda Aceh.

- Subsequently, a series of four major tsunamis was triggered, creating waves up to 30 metres (98 feet) high that spread as much as 2 km (1.2 miles) inland (see Fig. 3.2.2).

- Over a quarter of a million people were killed, a third of whom were children.

- The worst ever train disaster was caused by the tsunami in Sri Lanka. A train running along the western coast of the island was washed away by a wave, killing over 1700 people.

Fig. 3.2.2: People fleeing as the tsunami wave crashes ashore at Koh Roya, Andaman Islands

- It is estimated that the energy released in the form of shock waves from the earthquake epicentre was as much energy as the entire USA uses in 11 days. The earthquake caused the entire Earth's surface to move vertically by 1 centimetre (0.4 inches).

Longer-term effects

- The impact of the vast volumes of water pouring inland caused much of the coastline around the Indian Ocean to change shape. This can be seen on satellite photographs taken of the same stretch of coastline before and after the tsunami (see Fig. 3.2.3).

Fig. 3.2.3: Northern coast of Aceh province, Sumatra, before (left) and after (right), the tsunami

- Most coastal settlements in Indonesia and many in Thailand, Bangladesh, India and Sri Lanka were totally destroyed. Thousands of people died and over one million people were left homeless.

- In the days and weeks after the tsunami, water-borne diseases such as cholera and typhoid spread quickly due to the lack of fresh drinking water and sanitation.

- Many coastal marine areas became polluted with dead bodies, debris and industrial waste as the retreating tsunami waves dragged them out to sea. The tsunami waves also destroyed vast areas of coral. Together these events had the impact of reducing tourist numbers and the money and jobs tourism brings.

Human response

The global devastation of the tsunami created the need for a worldwide tsunami early warning system to prevent any future disasters on this scale. Such a system would involve **seismometers** placed on the sea floor along plate boundaries. When the seismometers sense **foreshocks** they would transmit a warning signal relayed to tsunami warning centres based in every Indian Ocean country. Such a system is now in place.

Planning laws along the Indian Ocean coast now require hotels to put car parks on the ground floor and accommodation on the first floor and above. In the event of a tsunami much of the destructive wave should then pass through the hotel, only destroying cars and leaving guests much safer.

All Indian Ocean countries have now developed tsunami evacuation procedures so that, given only a few minutes' warning, people know where to go and what to do. Such procedures encourage tourists and locals to seek higher ground by means of well marked evacuation routes. These drills are rehearsed regularly.

Other effects of earthquakes

Fortunately, few earthquakes trigger devastating tsunamis. Earthquakes in densely populated areas such as cities can cause buildings to collapse and crumble into the loosened ground (**liquefaction**) causing injury and death. However, the biggest danger immediately after an earthquake is usually fire, caused by broken gas pipes and exposed electricity cables. Emergency services may be unable to put out fires quickly because of severed water pipes, and may struggle to reach fires because of the damage done to roads.

In **LEDCs** particularly, diseases such as dysentery, hepatitis and cholera can spread if fresh water supplies are not restored quickly. Limited access, due to damaged or destroyed transport systems (roads, railways and airports), can often mean that the relief effort is slow. The financial cost of rebuilding the infrastructure can damage a country's economy for years.

Exercise 3B

1. Draw a well-labelled diagram to illustrate what led to the earthquake and resulting tsunami that devastated the Indian Ocean coastline on Boxing Day 2004.

2. Create a table with three columns: environmental effects, economic effects and social effects. List the effects of the tsunami.

3. Imagine that you and your family were living in Banda Aceh when the earthquake and tsunami struck. Write an account of the devastation that the tsunami has brought upon your home, your family and friends, and your local community.

4. Explain the meaning of each of the following terms:
   Richter scale
   epicentre
   liquefaction
   natural disaster

5. What can be done to prevent so many people dying should another tsunami hit the coastline of the Indian Ocean?

Extension question

6. 'The immediate and long-term effects of natural disasters are more pronounced in LEDCs.' Discuss this statement and refer to at least one example.

3.3 Syllabus example: Volcano in an MEDC, Mount Etna, Sicily 2001

Mount Etna is an extremely active volcano located in the eastern part of the Italian island of Sicily (see Fig. 3.1.2, page 80, and Fig. 3.3.1). At a height of 3350 metres (10,990 feet), it dominates the island. Although eruptions are not as large or devastating as those from other volcanoes in the world, its almost constant activity causes significant danger to the thousands of people who live and work on Etna's slopes. On 13th July 2001 one of the largest eruptions of Etna in recent years began.

Causes

Sicily lies on the boundary between two continental plates, the Eurasian plate and the African plate, which are moving past one another along most of the boundary. Scientists believe the African plate is being subducted under the Eurasian plate and that the plates appear to be acting as they would at a destructive plate boundary. This may explain volcanoes such as Vesuvius in Italy and Etna in Sicily.

Fig. 3.3.1: Satellite image of a smoke plume (brown centre) from Mount Etna during an eruption

Effects

The effects of a natural disaster, such as the eruption of Mount Etna, can be broadly split into two groups: the immediate effects and the longer term consequences.

Many of the effects can also fall into two or all three of the following groups:

- Environmental effects – the ways in which the landscape is damaged, for example, farmland and the surrounding countryside can be covered in thick, poisonous ash.

- Economic effects – the way in which property, transport and industry are affected and the cost of rebuilding this infrastructure.

- Social effects – the ways in which the people suffer injury, death and the destruction of their homes and family network.

Immediate effects

- On the morning of 13th July 2001 magma pushed its way up and through one of the volcano's vents. This movement of magma caused the south side of Etna to bulge, a process known as **deformation**, and led to a series of earthquakes.

- Over the next few days, lava bubbled up to the surface in the **crater** of the volcano and at several secondary cones and vents to the south and east of the main cone. Lava fountaining could be seen from the main cone (see Fig. 3.3.2).

Fig. 3.3.2: Lava fountaining from the crater of Mount Etna

- The 2001 eruption began in earnest on 17th July as huge plumes of ash poured from the crater and **volcanic bombs** were ejected. Lava flows streamed from vents on the south and east of Etna and headed slowly towards the tourist settlement of Nicolosi.

- Ash plumes, volcanic bombs and lava flows continued for the next 24 days. The lava did not reach any major settlements but did destroy roads, a scientific research station, a cable car and many ski lifts. The ash in the atmosphere and fallen ash on its runway forced Catania airport to close.

Longer-term effects

- Ash fall in the days and weeks following the eruption covered many of the vineyards that lined the slopes of Mount Etna, damaging or destroying the vines. These slopes are good for farming as the soil has been fertilised by the minerals weathered from previous eruptions (see Fig. 3.3.3). In the long term, volcanic eruptions can benefit farming communities but in the short term the ash can be devastating to a crop.

Fig. 3.3.3: Farming on the slopes of Mount Etna

- The lava flows from the 2001 eruption caused extensive damage to ski facilities and expensive repairs were required before the beginning of the winter season.

The warm lava fields remaining on Etna's slopes in the following months meant that snow did not settle the following winter, damaging the income generated from skiing.

- Ash or **tephra** (see Fig. 3.3.4) fell for several miles around the volcano, covering the city of Catania. The total cleaning cost to the city was estimated at over half a million pounds but the overall economic cost to Sicily has been much higher.

- The 2001 eruption of Mount Etna was highly publicised, with television crews reporting live from Etna's slopes. Many tourists watching the news cancelled their holidays to Sicily and, even, Italy!

- The media obsession with Etna during the summer of 2001 may, however, have been of benefit to the local economy in the long term. Every year increasing numbers of people visit Sicily hoping to witness another eruption. This tourism

Fig. 3.3.4: A column of ash rising from Mount Etna

benefits the local economy. The global awareness of Etna, brought about by the 2001 eruption, may have increased the number of tourist visitors to this part of Italy.

Human response

As spectacular and destructive as the 2001 eruption of Mount Etna was it did not, in fact, claim any lives. This is because, as an **MEDC**, Italy can afford a range of scientific equipment that constantly monitors Mount Etna and which is able accurately to predict when it will erupt.

Seismometers record changes in the shape of the volcano which can indicate when an eruption is likely to happen. There are also instruments that measure any increase in sulphur dioxide or carbon dioxide emissions. The Italian authorities also have access to satellite imaging that shows temperature changes on the slopes of Mount Etna.

Hazard maps are created from data recorded at previous eruptions. These maps indicate the urban areas that may be threatened in a future eruption. By studying hazard maps and monitoring the volcano the authorities can make accurate decisions about which areas to evacuate and when. In this way the risk to local people and tourists is significantly minimised although very little can be done to prevent destruction of property.

Other effects of volcanoes

The eruptions of Mount Etna produced large plumes of ash, volcanic bombs and slow-moving lava flows. However, although these hazards threatened property, they did not threaten life. Elsewhere in the world, particularly in tropical regions, hazards such as mudflows (**lahars**) and landslides triggered by volcanic eruptions can flow down valleys, covering villages with several metres of mud.

By far the most destructive and dangerous hazard during a volcanic eruption, however, is a **pyroclastic flow**, a fast-moving cloud of super-heated gas and rock (known as **tephra**) that can be released as a volcano erupts and which destroys everything in its path (see Fig. 3.3.5). Pyroclastic flows can travel at up to 200 km/hour (125 miles/hour) and can spread out many kilometres from the volcanic cone.

Fig. 3.3.5: Aerial view of a pyroclastic flow entering the sea from a volcanic eruption in the Soufriere Hills, Montserrat

Exercise 3C

1. Draw a flowchart to explain the events of the 2001 eruption of Mount Etna. Your flowchart should include the following statements rearranged into the correct order. These statements could be expanded and added to:

    Lava flows in the direction of Nicolosi.
    Ash and volcanic bombs are ejected on 17th July.
    Deformation of Mount Etna as magma rises.
    Many earthquakes are felt on 13th July.

2. What social and economic problems did the eruption cause at the time of the eruption and in the following weeks and months?

3. What can be done to predict and prepare for volcanic eruptions such as the event at Mount Etna in 2001?

4. Draw a map of Mount Etna as it would have appeared as it was erupting in 2001. You will need to do some research. Include the following labels:

    lava flows   **crater**
    volcanic bombs   **deformation**
    tephra   **city of Catania**
    ski lifts

5. Explain the meaning of the following terms and explain why they can be so dangerous:

    pyroclastic flow
    lahars

Extension question

6. Volcanic eruptions and earthquakes can have deadly results. Why do so many people continue to live in tectonically active areas which are potentially very dangerous? Refer to at least one example in your answer. You may need to do some research on the internet or in your library.

3.4 Predicting and preparing for earthquakes and volcanoes

There are a number of measures a country can take to predict earthquakes and volcanoes, and many steps that can be taken to prepare for them. However, these measures often require a great deal of money and organisation, so they can be adopted in wealthy MEDCs but are harder to apply in poorer LEDCs. This makes the people in LEDCs more vulnerable to the threats presented by earthquakes and volcanoes.

Predicting and preparing for earthquakes

Despite scientific developments, it remains extremely difficult to predict accurately where and when earthquakes may occur, other than expecting them to occur along plate boundaries. The following methods, however, can assist in these predictions:

- Regular, small earthquakes can occur along a conservative/sliding plate boundary, as the plates slide past each other causing friction and a build-up of stress which is periodically released. If these small earthquakes cease it may indicate the plates have locked. When the stress is suddenly released, a large earthquake may occur. In the hours and minutes before a large earthquake, smaller earthquakes called foreshocks may be felt, indicating that a big one is on its way. These shock waves are measured using a seismometer (see Fi. 3.4.1).

Fig. 3.4.1: Seismometer

- Scientists have also noticed that a gas called radon is often released in the hours before an earthquake. If a fault line along a plate boundary is monitored for radon emissions this may help to predict the location of an impending earthquake.

- Certain animals are very sensitive to movements in the ground and can react as they can feel foreshocks that humans cannot. It took over an hour for the Indian Ocean tsunami of 2004 to hit the coast of Thailand, but local elephants had already broken their chains and headed to higher ground as they felt the initial earthquake.

In LEDCs earthquakes that strike densely populated areas can kill many thousands of people. Buildings in LEDCs are often hastily built without following proper building regulations and consequently fall in on themselves (**pancaking**) even after small earthquakes (see Fig. 3.4.2). MEDCs can better afford to protect their buildings and to limit the damage and threat to life:

- A building made of concrete or brick is not particularly flexible, but if it is encased in a steel frame or shell it is able to twist and bend during an earthquake. This is called cross bracing and means the building is less likely to collapse.

Fig. 3.4.2: Building collapse after an earthquake in Pakistan

- Some buildings in LEDCs are made of wood which, while more flexible and less likely to collapse, can catch fire. Fire can quickly spread and, in LEDCs where emergency services are not equipped to deal with multiple fires, this can have a devastating effect. In MEDCs buildings are often equipped with sprinkler systems which put out fires before they spread.

- To enable a building to absorb much of the power of the shock waves emanating from an earthquake, it can be built with reinforced rubber foundations allowing it to move with the earthquake rather than collapse.

- A building can be protected by installing a counterweight on the top floor. This ensures the building stays stable even when the ground is shaking. Counterweights are expensive to install and therefore are used in MEDCs and NICs in buildings such as office blocks, which are often covered in glass, for example, Taipei 101, in China (see Fig. 3.4.3). To prevent injury and death these buildings are nearly always built using highly reinforced glass.

Fig. 3.4.3: Taipei 101, South East Asia

Predicting and preparing for volcanic eruptions

Predicting volcanic eruptions is much easier than predicting earthquakes because volcanoes give lots of clues that they might be about to erupt (see Fig. 3.4.4).

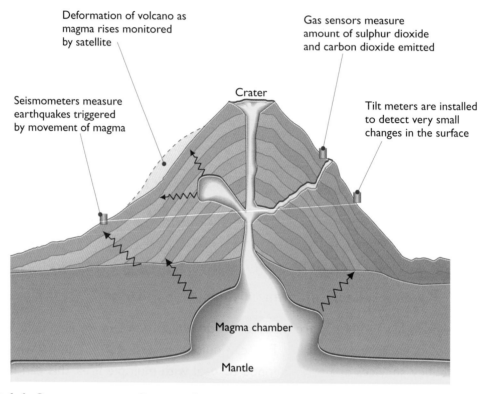

Fig. 3.4.4: *Systems to predict a volcanic eruption*

- A volcano will begin to deform (change shape) as the magma rises within it. This deformation can be seen by the naked eye but is more accurately monitored by satellites. **Tilt meters** are also used to measure deformation, for example on White Island, New Zealand.

- Scientists can place sensing equipment on and around the volcano to measure the levels of sulphur dioxide and carbon dioxide being emitted. A significant rise in the levels of these gases could mean an eruption is imminent.

- Seismometers can be placed on the slopes of a volcano. Before an eruption many earthquakes will occur as the volcano begins to change shape. On the day that Mount Etna erupted in 2001 more than 2000 separate earthquakes were measured.

Information about when a volcano is going to erupt means that people living in the immediate area can be evacuated. Using a combination of the methods above, scientists have successfully predicted many volcanic eruptions, particularly in MEDCs where appropriate scientific equipment is available. In LEDCs money is not always available for such equipment.

Despite developments in science it is still not easy to predict exactly when a volcano will erupt but there are several measures that can be taken to prepare for such an eventuality:

- Authorities can evacuate local residents based on scientific prediction and knowledge of how far lava flows have reached in past eruptions. This may be recorded on a hazard map.

- Many settlements on the slopes of volcanoes have large trenches built above them (lava dams) which will divert lava flows and lahars either side of the town or village should an eruption occur (see Fig. 3.4.5).

Fig. 3.4.5: Lava dam construction on the slopes of Mount Etna

- During an eruption water can be sprayed on slow-moving lava to cool it and slow its progress, especially if it is heading towards a settlement. In previous eruptions of Mount Etna the Italian airforce bombed lava flows to divert them. Resources to employ these tactics need to be prepared before an eruption.

Exercise 3D

1. Describe three methods that can be used to predict a volcanic eruption. Illustrate these methods with a diagram.

2. Draw a sketch of a typical skyscraper that you would find in many cities in MEDCs. Around your drawing add labels to indicate what technology could be used in the building to make it stable and safe during an earthquake. You will need to do some research for this question.

3. Explain the meaning of each of the following terms:
   foreshock
   pancaking
   seismometers
   deformation

4. Why is it much easier to prepare for an earthquake than to predict one?

5. Why do earthquakes kill more people in LEDCs than in MEDCs?

Extension question

6. 'Predictions of volcanic eruptions are more likely to be accurate than predictions of when or where an earthquake will occur.' Is this statement true? Use examples to justify your answer.

End of chapter activity

This game is a great way to learn the meaning of keywords. The teacher provides cards with keywords written on one side (these can be taken from the glossary to this chapter). Pairs compete to see who can describe and guess the highest number of keywords in a two minute period. In each pair, one person is **A**, the other is **B**. This is how to play:

1. The first pair comes forward and the teacher starts the stopwatch.

2. **A** takes a card and begins describing the keyword written on it (e.g. crust) to his or her partner **B**.

3. **A** cannot mention the keyword or variations of the keyword (e.g. crustation).

4. **A** cannot say it rhymes with another word (e.g. dust).

5. When **B** guesses the word, **B** takes a card and describes the keyword to **A**. **A** and **B** take it in turns to be the one describing the word.

6. Count how many keywords the pair guess in the two minute period.

7. Now it is the turn of another pair to do the same.

8. The winning pair is the one with the most correct keywords.

Glossary

Active volcano	A volcano that has erupted recently and could erupt again.
Collision plate boundary	An area where two continental plates collide and create fold mountains.
Conservative or sliding plate boundary	An area where two tectonic plates slide past each other, causing earthquakes.
Constructive plate boundary	An area where two oceanic or two continental plates move apart from each other creating volcanoes.
Continental plate	Crust that forms the continents. It is older, thicker and less dense than oceanic crust.
Convection currents	Flow of heat currents through the mantle.
Core	The centre of the Earth, believed to be solid and made of iron.
Crater	Top of a volcano from where most ash and lava is ejected.
Crust	The solid outer layer of the Earth, split into tectonic plates.
Deformation	The change in shape or bulging of a volcano just before it erupts, caused by rising magma.
Destructive plate boundary	An area where an oceanic plate slides beneath a continental plate, causing earthquakes and giving rise to volcanoes.
Dormant volcano	A volcano that has erupted in the last 2000 years but not recently.
Earthquake	A movement of the Earth's crust, which usually causes damage to property and risk to human life.
Epicentre	The point on the Earth's surface directly above the focus of an earthquake.
Extinct volcano	A volcano that has not erupted in the last 2000 years and is not expected to erupt again.
Fault	A line of weakness running through plates extended from plate boundaries.

Foreshock	A smaller earthquake preceding a larger or main earthquake.
Lahar	Mudflow composed of pyroclastic material and water.
Lava	Molten rock flowing out of the ground from a volcano.
LEDC	Less Economically Developed Country.
Liquefaction	The break-up of the ground into smaller pieces during an earthquake, causing buildings to sink and collapse.
Lock	When two plates catch on each other as they pass. Pressure builds up which will later be released as an earthquake.
Magma	Molten rock below the Earth's surface.
Mantle	The semi-solid largest layer of the Earth, kept under pressure by the crust.
MEDC	More Economically Developed Country.
Oceanic plate	Crust that lines the ocean floor. It is younger, thinner and denser than continental crust.
Pancaking	The term used to describe the collapse of a building during an earthquake.
Plate boundary	The area where two plates meet, usually causing earthquakes and/or volcanic eruptions.
Pyroclastic flow	A fast moving cloud of boiling gases and ash ejected from a volcano.
Richter scale	A logarithmic scale measuring the strength of an earthquake.
Seismometer	A sensitive, scientific instrument used to measure earthquakes.
Subduction zone	An area where an oceanic plate slides beneath a continental plate at a destructive plate boundary, triggering earthquakes.
Tectonic plate	A large section of the Earth's crust, either oceanic or continental.
Tephra	Another word for ash.

Tilt meter   A device that measures the amount of deformation of the crust around a volcanic vent.

Tsunami   A tidal wave caused by an undersea earthquake or volcano.

Volcanic bombs   Solidified pieces of lava ejected by a volcano during an eruption.

Volcano   A cone-shaped mountain made up of lava and ash from previous eruptions.

Chapter 4: Economic activities

In this chapter we will look at:

- How jobs are categorised into different groups.

- What makes particular industries locate in certain places.

- The globalisation of industry and its effect on LEDCs.

- The types of farming in Britain and where they are found.

- What factors influence the location of a secondary industry.

- Why tourism is such a large global industry and how it influences Britain in a positive and negative way.

- Two global economic activity case studies: Toyota car manufacturing in Britain and Nike sportswear manufacturing in Asia.

4.1 Putting jobs into different categories

The employment structure

A country with a successful **economy** has a large proportion of its population in **employment** in a wide range of jobs within a great number of economic activities. These economic activities are classified into four categories according to their stage in the process of production.

Fig. 4.1.1: Primary activity – fishing

Primary activities

Jobs in a primary activity are involved in extracting **raw materials** directly from the earth or sea. There are five main **primary activities**: farming, fishing (see Fig. 4.1.1), forestry, mining and oil and natural gas drilling. These **industries** employ millions of people worldwide and are the economic activities that formed the foundation of ancient economies. These activities are still a vital part of modern economies.

Secondary activities

People employed in **secondary activities** use the raw materials produced by the primary industries to **manufacture** a product. Manufacturing usually takes place in a factory (see Fig. 4.1.2). The products that are made include electrical items, cars, furniture and clothes and include industries such as oil refining and food processing or packaging.

Fig. 4.1.2: Secondary activity – cheese factory

Fig. 4.1.3: Tertiary activity – firefighter

Tertiary activities

Those employed in **tertiary activities** sell the products manufactured by secondary industries to the public in shops such as supermarkets, department stores and high street chain stores. Tertiary workers can also provide **services** to the public, including free services such as the police, fire or health service, or private services such as entertainment, **tourism** or finance.

Quaternary activities

The role of those employed in **quaternary activities** is to research and develop new products, often for companies producing hi-tech goods such as computers and mobile phones. Scientists researching products such as medicines are another example of people working in a quaternary activity (see Fig. 4.1.4). The information industries and consultancy are also sometimes included in this category.

Fig. 4.1.4: Quaternary activity – a chemist working in a laboratory

Identifying economic activities on OS maps

It is necessary to be able to identify different economic activities on OS maps.

Farms, woodland plantations and quarries or mines are good examples of common primary activities to be found on an OS map.

Secondary activities (industries) are indicated by *industrial estate* (or sometimes *ind estate*), *factory* or *wks* (short for *works*).

The easiest type of industry to find examples of on OS maps is tertiary industry. Maps that show settlements will include examples of services such as hospitals, schools, train stations, sports centres, post offices, public houses, etc.

Tourist attractions and facilities are often coloured blue on OS maps. Tourism is an important tertiary industry.

Use the map of Bedford in Fig. 4.1.5 on page 107 to identify different examples of primary, secondary and tertiary industries.

Employment structures in MEDCs and LEDCs

If you conducted a survey in your class to discover how parents were employed, it would probably reveal that many of them were employed in tertiary industry (bankers, lawyers, doctors). Britain has a very high proportion of its population employed in this sector because it is a wealthy **MEDC** the population of which can afford public services (healthcare, education, police) and private services (shops, financial services, entertainment), all of which are catered for by tertiary industries.

In **LEDCs** there tend to be lower levels of employment overall, and a higher proportion of employment in primary and secondary industries. Due to fewer education facilities in LEDCs the majority of the population may not possess the skills required for employment in tertiary industries. As the population is poor, it is less able to afford tertiary products and services, resulting in a reduced market for these services.

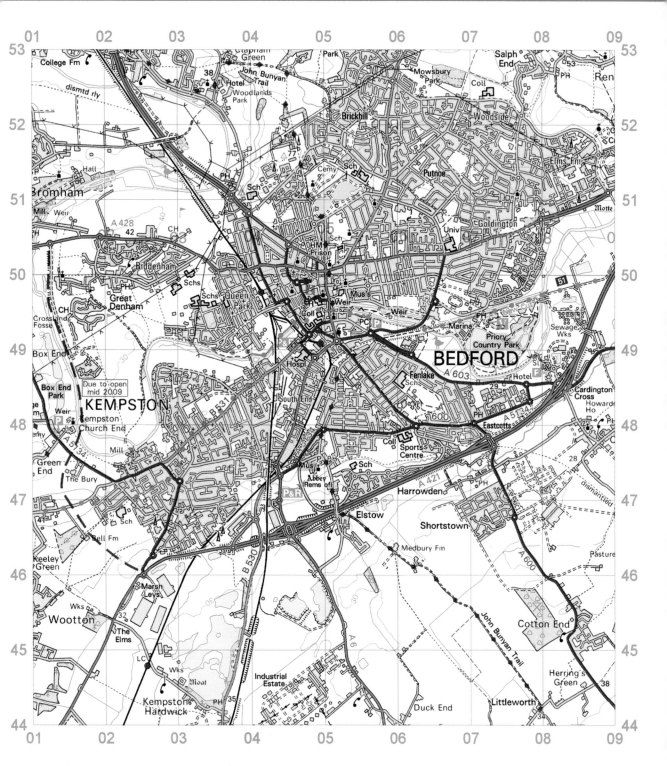

Fig. 4.1.5: OS map extract of Bedford

Location of industries

Over the last two centuries industries such as steel and iron manufacture, and mills (paper and woollen), often grew up around the source of their raw materials. For example, paper mills were found near a source of wood, and woollen mills near big sheep farming areas. Steel manufacturers were found near coal fields (for their power supply).

However, things have changed and many industries in Britain today are much freer to locate wherever they like. The traditional need to be close to raw materials, energy supply and the market is no longer as important. With greatly improved transport and communication now available, the two most important factors of location have become access and transport hubs, for example ports, railway terminals and airports, and the cost of labour. Industries can now search the world to find the lowest cost of labour.

Sometimes people say 'the world is getting smaller' or describe the world as a 'global village'.

The increase in trade and the sharing of ideas and cultures throughout the world is called **globalisation**. This has been made possible by improvements in transport and communications. Some companies have taken advantage of these improvements to move their operations to different parts of the world where there are favourable **location factors** (such as low labour costs). These companies are called **transnational corporations** (TNCs) and are often large, wealthy and powerful organisations.

The location of TNCs in an LEDC can have a significant effect on the people and the country's economy. Some of these effects are positive:

- A reduction in trade taxes means that companies in LEDCs find it easier to trade their products with other LEDCs and more recently with MEDCs.

- Huge improvements in transport and demand for global holiday destinations from people in MEDCs means that many LEDCs are now generating a high income from tourism. For example, many Asian and African countries such as Thailand and Egypt generate money from tourists through a tourist tax paid to the government which then invests the money in developing facilities such as schools, roads and hospitals.

- Many TNCs that decide to locate their factories in LEDCs provide jobs for local people who may otherwise be unemployed.

However, globalisation also has disadvantages:

- Governments in LEDCs have often encouraged the growth of industry without considering the environmental effects. China, for example, contains 16 out of the 20 most polluted cities in the world.

- Some TNCs have located their factories in LEDCs in order to exploit the low wages in these countries and thereby increase their profits. Often factory workers are paid below the average wage of workers in developed countries, and forced to work very long hours in poor conditions where they may not have access to drinking water (see Fig. 4.1.6). In some factories child labour is used, even when it is illegal.

Fig. 4.1.6: Poor conditions in some LEDC factories

- The rapid increase in TNCs locating their factories in LEDCs means that many LEDCs are becoming dependent on these companies for jobs. Many local people, who may have previously worked for local companies or as farmers, take jobs with TNCs.

Exercise 4A

1. Create four list headings as below:

   Primary　　　　　**Secondary**　　　　　**Tertiary**　　　　　**Quaternary**

   Now list the following jobs under the correct headings:

Fire fighter	Car assembly worker	Inventor
Farmer	Oil drill operator	Builder
Lawyer	Professional footballer	Dentist
Research scientist	Textile factory worker	

2. The following phrases all relate to the oil industry in Britain. Match them up to the correct type of industry: primary, secondary, tertiary or quaternary.
   (a) Researching new, more environmentally friendly fuels
   (b) Drilling for oil in the North Sea
   (c) Refining oil at processing plants on the east coast of Scotland to create petrol and other by-products
   (d) Selling petrol at petrol stations throughout Britain and Europe

3. Look at the map of Bedford in Fig. 4.1.5 on page 107. For each of the following types of industry, find an example, name the example and give a six figure grid reference for the example you have identified.
   (a) Primary industry
   (b) Secondary industry
   (c) Tertiary industry

4. List examples of primary, secondary and tertiary industries in your local area. You may need to look at a local map or conduct some research on the internet to help you answer this question.

5. (a) What does the term 'globalisation' mean?
   (b) List two positive effects of globalisation on LEDCs and two negative effects.

Extension question

6. Why do transnational companies (TNCs) often locate their manufacturing sectors in LEDCs?

4.2 Examples of primary, secondary and tertiary activities (industries)

Farming: A primary industry

Around 10,000 years ago humans developed the skills to grow crops from seeds and breed animals. The primary industry of farming, or **agriculture**, was born. The different types of farming can be split into three groups: arable, pastoral and mixed.

- **Arable farming** involves growing crops such as barley, wheat and oilseed rape. Arable farming also includes **market gardening**, which involves growing fruit and vegetables, often on a small scale and sometimes in controlled greenhouse conditions.

- **Pastoral farming** involves breeding or rearing animals for their meat or other produce. Sheep, cows, pigs, chickens and turkeys are all are bred for their meat. Poultry (chickens and turkeys) are also reared to produce eggs, and cows are often bred for their milk (dairy farming).

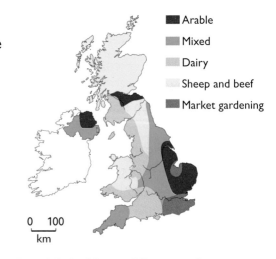

Fig. 4.2.1: Map of Britain showing the distribution of farming types

- **Mixed farming** is the use of a single farm for multiple purposes, for example arable and pastoral farming. Mixed farming on a small scale, **subsistence agriculture**, is common in parts of Africa, Asia and South America. This is a method of farming in which farmers plan to grow only enough food to feed the family, pay taxes or other dues, and perhaps provide a small surplus to sell.

Fig. 4.2.1 (see page 110) shows that most pastoral farming in Britain is located in the north-west and most arable farming in the south-east. This is a generalised map. In reality, the **distribution** of farming types is much more complex.

Physical factors that influence a farmer

The distribution of farming types as shown in Fig. 4.2.1 is due to the **physical factors** that influence the type of farming that is appropriate in a particular region. These factors are: relief, soil, temperature and rainfall.

Relief

The relief aspects of the land (its shape and height) affect what type of farming is chosen. Flat land is suitable for arable farming as machinery can be used on it. Steep land is better for pastoral sheep farming because sheep can graze on steep slopes.

Soil

The depth and quality of soil have an effect on the type of farming. If the soil is deep and **fertile** it will be more suitable for arable farming, if shallow and lacking in fertility it may be better for pastoral or mixed farming.

Temperature

The temperature of a local area affects the type of farming. Some crops are damaged by freezing temperatures; therefore colder, highland areas may not be as suitable for arable farming as warmer lowland areas.

Rainfall

The amount of rainfall an area receives is a crucial physical factor. Although both animals and crops need water, too much rainfall can destroy crops by encouraging disease or causing flooding.

Pastoral farming is more common in the north and north-west of Britain where land is steeper, soils are thinner, and the climate is often colder and wetter. The south and east of Britain is flatter, the soils tend to be deeper and richer and the climate is warmer and drier, so there tends to be more arable farming, particularly cereal crops.

Human factors that influence a farmer

The type of farming that a farmer chooses to practise and the exact location of a farm may also be influenced by **human factors**: farm size, technology, accessibility to the market and government help.

Farm size

The size of a farm is an important factor. Pastoral farming requires a large amount of land for the animals to graze on. By contrast, arable farmers can sow crops densely in a small area and practise **intensive farming**.

Technology

The amount of technology used on a farm varies according to the type of farming. Arable farms tend to be farmed intensively, so a great deal of money is spent on fertilisers and special machinery such as combine harvesters (see Fig. 4.2.2). Pastoral farmers tend to practise **extensive farming** with less money spent on machinery.

Fig. 4.2.2: Arable farming often means spending money on special machinery

Accessibility to the market

A farm's profit will be dependent on how close the farm is to its market. It is beneficial for a farm to be close and well linked by roads and motorways to a big market. Farms that produce **perishable goods** (items that go bad quickly such as fruit and milk) need to be located close to their markets.

Government help

A government can encourage certain types of farming if it feels there is market demand. For example, dairy farmers are given **grants** and **subsidies** (financial assistance to guarantee a minimum income). Farmers may adopt a particular type of farming if government grants make it more profitable.

Extension topic: The history of farming in Britain

From the beginning of agriculture, thousands of years ago, until quite recently, only minor changes in farming methods were developed. In many LEDCs, farming is still carried on in the same way as it was hundreds of years ago. However, in Britain and other MEDCs during the mid to latter part of the 20th century, farming changed significantly with the development of machinery, **pesticides** and fertilisers. Farms have become more commercial as they have merged to form fewer but larger farms.

Since the middle of the 20th century farmers have found it more difficult to stay in business due to competition from foreign producers. Today the **European Union (EU)**, along with the British government, helps different groups of farmers to stay in business by providing them with grants and subsidies. This support for farmers has, in the past, created overproduction of agricultural produce within Britain and other European countries. **Surpluses** were produced. To overcome this waste, farmers are now given **quotas** limiting the amount of produce, such as milk, they can sell within the EU. **Diversification** has also been encouraged (where farmers change what they use their land for) and land can be left **fallow** (idle or uncultivated) for a number of years.

In order to diversify, some farmers have sold parts of their land to be developed for housing or industry. Many farmers have chosen to keep the land, as it may become more economical to cultivate in future. Others have developed income-generating activities such as golf courses, riding schools, paintballing centres and campsites.

Secondary industries

Location factors for secondary industry

There is a huge variety of secondary industries, manufacturing or processing all sorts of goods, from ships to clothes to electronic items. This variety means that many different location factors can influence where a factory is situated, including: raw materials, site proximity to market, labour supply, power source and transport links.

Raw materials

Some secondary industries manufacture products that are made from heavy raw materials which are difficult or expensive to transport; for example, a masonry factory or a paper mill (see Fig. 4.2.3). Others use raw materials that are perishable, such as food in food processing factories. In both cases these secondary industries are ideally located close to the raw materials they use.

Fig. 4.2.3: Paper mill

The site

All secondary industries look for the best value site for their factory, whether it is a small unit on an industrial estate or a factory that covers a huge area. Generally, land is cheaper the further north you travel within Britain and, on a local scale, land tends to be cheaper the further you travel away from city centres.

Fig. 4.2.4: Newspaper press, Canary Wharf, London

Flat ground is the best option for the site of a factory as it is much more expensive to build on uneven or steep land.

Proximity to the market

It is valuable for some secondary industries to be close to their market. This reduces the transport costs of sending goods to market and is useful when it is necessary to deliver goods quickly. Newspaper printers tend to be located in major cities so their newspapers can be quickly and easily distributed to the majority of their customers (see Fig. 4.2.4). Assembly industries, such as car manufacturing, are also often located near their markets or close to good transport routes.

Labour supply

If a factory requires many manual workers to operate machinery it is better for it to be located near a large **urban** area which can supply the workers (**labour**). Indeed a company may choose to locate its factory in a certain country because there is a good supply of labour there.

Modern manufacturing industries producing hi-tech goods such as computers and mobile phones, or specialist secondary industries such as aircraft assembly may need a small but more skilled labour force. These industries tend to locate near cities with universities where such skilled workers can be more easily recruited.

Power source

Many early industries grew up in locations near fast-flowing rivers, and used their power to run machinery (see Fig. 4.2.5). The **textile industry** positioned its mills on the highland rivers of Yorkshire and Lancashire during the 19th century to take advantage of this natural power source. Many of these mills have now been converted into modern housing or offices and some are museums celebrating this period of Britain's industrial history.

Power is rarely a consideration for industry in Britain today since electricity is accessible through the **national grid** in all but the most remote of locations.

Fig. 4.2.5: Cromford Mill, Peak District, Derbyshire

Transport links

The ability to transport manufactured goods to their various markets is an important location factor. Traditionally goods were transported by canal, rail or sea, therefore locations near these facilities were popular. Today most goods that are sold in Europe are transported by road, so being near a motorway junction is more important.

Extension topic: Why are location factors changing with time?
During the **Industrial Revolution** industry grew around power sources such as rivers and raw materials such as coal. Other industries then developed in these locations giving rise to the growth in urban areas that cover large areas of the UK today. In the last 30 years the world has experienced a new revolution that has changed the location factors that influence many secondary industries. The **technological revolution**, generated from the invention of the microchip, has led to the manufacture of **hi-tech goods** such as mobile phones and computers, that are very small, easily transported and sold on a global market.

Hi-tech firms are often referred to as **footloose** (they are not tied to one particular location). For example, they do not need to be near to a supply of heavy raw materials. In order for hi-tech firms, such as Microsoft, Nokia and Apple, to continue to develop new technologies and products, they prefer to locate near universities with which they can work on new product development. Hi-tech firms also cluster in order to share ideas and can often be found together on **science parks**. (Fig. 4.2.5.) These are purpose-built developments of industrial units and offices located on sites with some or all of the following advantages:

- good access: motorway junction, mainline train station nearby, airport within 50 kilometres (30 miles)

- newly built, high quality industrial units/offices

- landscaped grounds and gardens

- leisure facilities: sports centre, golf course, etc

- room for expansion

- university nearby

- large car parking facilities.

Fig. 4.2.5: Science park

Tertiary industries

Extension topic: The growth of tourism
The dictionary defines a tourist as 'a person who travels for pleasure' and tourism as 'the business of organising and providing services for tourists'. The World Tourism Organization (WTO) has further defined tourists as 'visitors who stay in the country

visited for at least one night'. Today tourism is one of the world's largest tertiary industries employing millions of people in both MEDCs and LEDCs. The WTO estimated that, in 2008, 922 million tourist visits were made, generating US$944 billion.

Tourism really began in the 19th century when wealthy aristocrats were encouraged to make the Grand Tour, a cultural exploration of the major European cities. During the period of the Industrial Revolution, factory workers were allowed only a few days' holiday a year, usually in the summer, when they would travel to British coastal resorts such as Blackpool (see Fig. 4.2.6). However, it was not until the second half of the 20th century that overseas tourism became an affordable opportunity for the average person in Britain.

Fig. 4.2.6: Blackpool at the height of its popularity

During the 1970s mass tourism began as **package holidays** to European destinations such as Spain and Greece were sold. Rapid growth in tourism has continued (see Fig. 4.2.7) due to improvements in transport such as the construction of the Channel Tunnel, as well as the availability and affordability of low cost airline flights within, and beyond, Europe. Despite catastrophes such as the 11th September 2001 terrorist attacks on the USA, and the Indian Ocean tsunami on 26th December 2004, the number of tourists continues to rise. This provides great benefits for many people but also causes problems for local people and their environment.

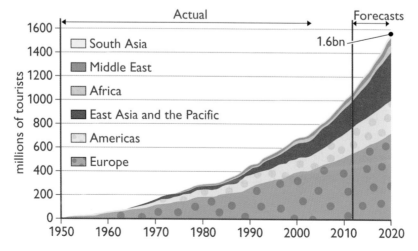

Fig. 4.2.7: The growth of global tourism

How tourism can benefit an area

Tourism can be one of the most profitable tertiary industries. All tourists stay at least one night in their chosen holiday destination and therefore spend money at a hotel, bed and breakfast or campsite. Tourists also spend in other ways within the area they are visiting, including at restaurants, local attractions or on organised tours (see Fig. 4.2.8). As well as bringing money and jobs to an area, tourists

Fig. 4.2.8: Making money from tourists

can also bring improved **infrastructure**. This benefits local people who can use the facilities that are built to attract tourists, for example, new roads and airports, leisure activities (health centres, golf courses, etc), new shopping centres and entertainment facilities. In LEDCs many villages that previously lacked drainage, electricity and fresh water supplies now have them as a result of infrastructure developments for tourists.

How tourism benefits a country's economy

All companies involved in tourism (airlines, hotel chains, travel agents, etc) have to pay taxes on their profits to the government. In this way the economy of a country benefits from money generated by tourism. The money can then be invested in education, healthcare and other services, as well as developing existing and new tourist resorts. Some places may also apply a small percentage tourist tax to tourist accommodation or charge tourists for entering or departing their country.

Many LEDCs remain poor because there is not enough employment for the increasing population. However, tourism can benefit these economies by reducing unemployment.

In the second half of the 20th century southern European countries such as Greece, Spain and Italy attracted many tourists with their sandy beaches, warm Mediterranean climate and interesting culture. These countries, which were once poor, are now wealthy MEDCs partly due to the economic benefits tourism has brought. More recently poorer countries such as Egypt, Kenya and Thailand have developed tourist facilities in order to benefit their economies. However, political unrest in these countries has, at times, damaged tourism and the consequent income.

How tourism can harm an area

Despite its distinct advantages, tourism can create problems for the local environment and also present difficulties for local residents.

Environmental problems

Many tourists ultimately arrive at a tourist destination in cars or tourist buses which emit carbon dioxide causing pollution and staining local historic buildings. Aeroplanes, which bring tourists from other countries, are also highly polluting.

In the rush to make money from tourism, countries do not always carefully plan tourist developments. The beautiful landscape that attracted tourists can often be spoilt (**visual pollution**). A good example of this is the Costa del Sol in Spain, which has been covered in rows of apartment blocks (see Fig. 4.2.9).

Fig. 4.2.9: Torremolinos, Costa del Sol, Spain

Even sections of land that were once wildlife habitats have been developed. The loss of habitat drives away animals, and birds no longer migrate there to breed. Large numbers of visitors to sensitive habitats can sometimes scare away the very animals they have come to see.

Increasingly, tourists are more considerate about the environment in which they are staying and have come to enjoy. However, littering remains a problem, especially in the larger tourist centres. Discarded tin cans and plastic items present a danger to wildlife and take hundreds if not thousands of years to **biodegrade** (the process by which organic materials are broken down by living organisms).

Problems for local residents

In some LEDCs private land or land belonging to local communities has been used for tourist facilities and accommodation. Local people have been forced out of their homes or have lost their only form of income when farmland has been used for tourism.

In Britain many tourist centres are small towns or villages located in beautiful countryside. Although these areas may make money from tourism, they can also suffer from overcrowding in the height of

Fig. 4.2.10: Traffic congestion in the pretty Cotswold village of Burford, Oxfordshire

summer. Narrow roads become congested with the volume of traffic that tourism brings (see Fig. 4.2.10, page 119).

Because many tourist destinations are attractive places to live, people from other areas often buy holiday homes there. This can have two effects:

- Prices increase to such a high level that local people struggle to buy houses in their local community.

- Because many of the holiday houses or flats are not occupied for most of the year, such places tend to lose their sense of community. Over time local shops and services may close down because the income from **seasonal jobs** is not sufficient.

In many European countries, small coastal villages have grown into large tourist centres with many bars and nightclubs catering for young people on holiday. Local residents often suffer the consequences of **noise pollution** and petty crime. In many overseas tourist resorts the local culture has changed too. In some areas the influence of English-speaking tourists has meant that locals often speak English more than they speak their own language (see Fig. 4.2.11).

Fig. 4.2.11: Nightlife in Ibiza

Remind yourself about the effect of tourism in the Peak District National Park by looking back at Chapter 2, Section 2.2, page 53.

Exercise 4B

1. (a) Describe the distribution of farming types in Britain. You may wish to add a simple annotated sketch of Britain with your answer.

   (b) Explain the pattern you have described in part (a) by linking the distribution of farming types with different physical factors.

2. Explain the meaning of each of the following terms:

   intensive farming   **extensive farming**

   subsidies   **surplus**

   subsistence agriculture

3. Match the following secondary industries with the following location factors:

    Location factor   **Industry**
    Close to raw materials   Computer software development
    Near a skilled labour supply   Fruit and vegetable growing
    Close to the market   Large car manufacturing plant
    Large and flat site for a factory   Stone mason

4. (a) Why is it important for most secondary industries to be close to a motorway junction or a port?
    (b) Why is power supply no longer important for most secondary industries?

5. (a) Describe the data shown in Fig 4.2.7 (page 117). Remember to quote figures from the graph and describe the pattern you can see.
    (b) Explain at least three reasons for the pattern you have identified in part (a).

Extension questions

6. How can some of the environmental problems tourism creates for locals be overcome? Identify three environmental problems and as many solutions for each problem as you can.

7. The importance of location factors for secondary industry has changed over time since the Industrial Revolution and varies between types of secondary industry. Explain, using example industries, why this is the case.

8. 'The present growth in tourism is sustainable due to LEDCs developing tourism.' Discuss this statement using examples to illustrate your argument.

4.3 Syllabus example: The Toyota car plant at Burnaston

Car manufacturing is one of the world's biggest secondary industries. It employs large labour forces in different countries throughout the world. During the 20th century car manufacturing was mainly located in the USA and Europe where companies such as General Motors, Ford and Volkswagen made and sold vehicles for their own markets. Today, like many other large industries, car manufacturing has experienced globalisation. Cars are being made by a wide range of companies, particularly those based in Asian countries such as Japan, for markets in hundreds of different countries. It is an incredibly competitive market so transnational companies such as Toyota need to plan carefully where to locate their factories.

Toyota is the fifth largest company in the world and the largest manufacturer of cars, with factories in 26 different countries worldwide (see Fig. 4.3.1) making it a highly successful TNC. Much of Toyota's global success has been credited to its highly efficient management structure and assembly techniques,

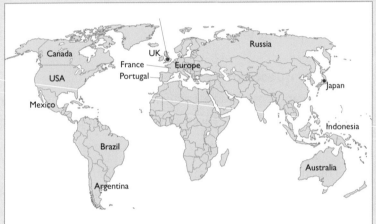

Fig 4.3.1: Location of some of the major Toyota factories

such as the 'just in time' method of production. Parts are delivered to the assembly line at the moment they are needed, which avoids storing parts, which can be expensive. The company crosses three sectors of the employment structure:

- Secondary workers **assemble** (put together) the pre-manufactured parts of the cars on an assembly line in Toyota's factories.

- Quaternary workers are employed to research, develop and design new cars.

- Tertiary workers sell Toyota cars at dealerships throughout the world.

Hybrid cars

In 1997 Toyota introduced its first hybrid car – the Toyota Prius (see Fig. 4.3.2). These cars use a traditional petrol- or diesel-fuelled combustion engine to generate power but an electric battery is charged when using this power source, which can be used to power the car at other times (typically when cruising or at low speed). The electric battery is also charged when going down hill or decelerating. By May 2007, Toyota had sold one million hybrid cars worldwide.

Fig. 4.3.2: The Toyota Prius

Toyota's reasons for moving car assembly to Britain

Toyota is a Japanese company and its headquarters and much of its car production remain in Japan. However, with an ever-increasing demand for its cars in Europe, Toyota decided to reduce transport costs and locate a car assembly plant in Europe to serve this market. The European market at this time was the largest in the world and Toyota was already selling 400,000 vehicles in Europe during the late 1980s.

Instead of locating the new car assembly plant in central Europe, Toyota decided that Britain would be the best country for its factory. This decision was made for several reasons:

- Britain had a history of car manufacturing, and therefore had labour with the appropriate skills to work in its factory.

- Despite being an island, Britain has excellent transport links to the rest of Europe.

- Britain has a large market for cars, therefore many cars that would be manufactured in Britain would also be sold in Britain.

- Car plants assemble parts, or **components**, at their factories. Britain already had many component manufacturers that could supply a Toyota factory with the parts it needed.

Toyota's reasons for choosing Burnaston

After deciding that Britain would be the host country for its factory, Toyota then had to decide where in Britain would be best and most profitable for the company.

After analysing several sites, Burnaston in Derbyshire (Fig. 4.3.3) was chosen for the following reasons:

Fig. 4.3.3: Burnaston, Derbyshire

- Burnaston is centrally located in Britain and served well by the M6 and M1 motorways, so is an ideal location from which to transport the manufactured cars to markets in Britain.

- There are many component factories located in the West Midlands which could supply a Toyota factory.

- Although centrally located in Britain the price of land in Derbyshire is relatively cheap, certainly compared to the prices of sites in the south of England.

- The large site at Burnaston was ideal because the land was flat and even after the factory had been built there would still be room for expansion (see Fig. 4.3.4). This proved the right choice because Toyota did indeed expand in January 2001, increasing output from 100,000 to 170,000 cars per year.

Similar location factors were considered when Toyota opened its Deeside factory in North Wales in 1992. In 2011, the Deeside factory employed 486 people, and the larger Burnaston factory employed 2662. However, due to the economic down turn that began in 2008, Toyota began to reduce working hours at its UK factories and in Japan closed its factories for eleven days to reduce output and stocks of unsold cars.

How Toyota benefits the local community

A committed workforce and innovative ideas have driven Japanese industry in recent years. These qualities are incorporated into the production processes employed by Toyota and are used in the UK factories. Toyota was well aware that to be successful at Burnaston it needed to gain the respect and support of the local community, by not only providing well-paid jobs but also offering excellent working conditions to its workers and consulting carefully with local government about the building of the plant.

Fig. 4.3.4: Toyota's factory at Burnaston

After its expansion in 2001, Toyota employed around 2850 people. This helped to reduce unemployment in the local area and provided school leavers with a possible career. These workers are provided with very favourable working conditions which have helped to create a stable and happy workforce. These conditions include:

- Generous shift allowance
- Paid overtime
- 25 days' paid annual holiday (plus bank holidays)
- Private healthcare
- Pension
- Life assurance
- Attractive car plan
- Free workwear
- Subsidised restaurants
- Workplace nursery

Toyota's decision to locate its plant in the West Midlands has encouraged the development of further component manufacturers in the area which has been good for the local economy. Having seen Toyota's success at Burnaston other TNCs are now likely to choose Britain, and possibly the West Midlands, to locate their manufacturing plants.

Exercise 4C

1. Why did Toyota choose to locate its car factory in Britain? Use the terms below in your answer.

   market   **component manufacturers**
   skilled labour **transport**

2. On a blank outline map of Britain locate Burnaston. Draw arrows pointing to Burnaston and write labels to show why this particular site was a good choice for Toyota.

3. Explain the meaning of each of the following words:

   labour   **Industrial Revolution**
   hi-tech goods   **science parks**

4. What benefits does Toyota bring to the community of Burnaston and the surrounding area?

5. Imagine that you are working for the recruitment department at Toyota's Burnaston car manufacturing plant. You want to attract the best workers to come to work in your plant. Create an advertisement to go in a national newspaper explaining the advantages of working for Toyota.

Extension question

6. Explain what you think governments can do to attract TNCs such as Toyota to their countries.

4.4 Syllabus example: Nike textile supplier factories in South East Asia

Nike is an example of a transnational corporation (TNC). It was founded in 1964 and was named 'Nike' by the owners Bill Bowerman and Philip Knight after previously being called Blue Ribbon Sports. It is one of the world's leading sports retailers, selling shoes, clothes and sports equipment (see Fig. 4.4.1).

Fig. 4.4.1: Nike products

Where are Nike's suppliers located?

Nike has its headquarters in Oregon, USA and has more than 700 supplier factories or offices located in 45 countries outside the USA. No Nike clothing or footwear is made in the USA, although a majority of its sales are to markets in the USA, Canada and Europe.

Unlike Toyota, whose factories are run and owned by the Toyota company, Nike contracts other companies to make its products and therefore has no need to invest in factory building. The manufacture of shoes and clothing is **labour intensive**, so it

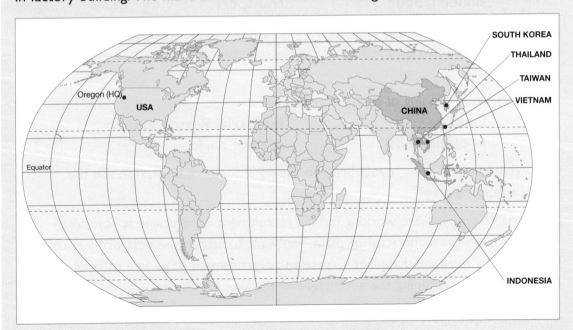

Fig. 4.4.2: Location of Nike supplier factories and offices

is important for Nike to choose suppliers with lower labour costs. Labour costs are lower in LEDCs than in MEDCs, so it is advantageous for Nike to have its products manufactured in countries such as Indonesia, China, Vietnam and Thailand (see Fig. 4.4.2, page 126). Land is also cheaper in LEDCS, so suppliers pay less for the land on which they build their factories and there is easy access to global markets. Nike can also change its suppliers to take advantage of the labour in a particular area.

For example, in Vietnam, one of the world's poorest countries, textile manufacturing is the fastest growing industry and provides employment for approximately 30,000 people, most of whom are young women (see Fig 4.4.3).

The effect of globalisation on TNCs

Globalisation has enabled TNCs such as Nike to develop into the huge brand names they are today. Nike has significant influence across the world with over 25,000 people worldwide employed in the manufacturing, supply, selling, and footwear research sectors.

Globalisation has brought improved transport, which enables TNCs to:

- move goods easily and quickly from LEDCs to MEDCs
- fly staff around the world for meetings and to visit sites.

Fig. 4.4.3: Women working in the textile industry

Improved technology enables TNCs to:

- keep in contact with their offices and factories worldwide using email and mobile phones
- reach an increasingly diverse market through advertising on television, in magazines and on the internet.

The effect of globalisation on LEDCs

Negative effects

Due to extreme poverty and a lack of education people in LEDCs are in desperate need of jobs. Therefore they are prepared to accept a low wage which may not give them enough to live on. Often they work very long hours in poor conditions. In MEDCs, by contrast, unions would insist on a **living wage** and reasonable working conditions.

For example, a textile worker in an LEDC may only be paid US$1.60 a day but a meal may cost about 60–70 cents, which means the worker can only afford two meals per day. Therefore, there will be little remaining for accommodation. As many as ten people may sleep, eat and wash in a one room hut. Working conditions in the factories are often very unpleasant. Hundreds of people may be working long hours in a small space, with poor ventilation and limited access to drinking water. These factories are therefore called **sweatshops**.

Extreme poverty and lack of government **regulation** can mean that TNCs are able to use child labour (see Fig. 4.4.4).

Environmental damage and pollution may also occur as there are few laws in LEDCs to ensure TNCs protect the environment.

What is being done to prevent TNCs exploiting LEDCs?

Many organisations are trying to halt the abuse of labour in LEDCs. For example, the Clean Clothes Campaign is an international organisation whose aim is to end labour abuses in the clothes industry. The Campaign, for example, looks closely at operations in Asia (particularly Thailand), India and China and campaigns for better wages and fair working conditions in accordance with standards set by the International Labour Organization.

In 2009, Nike began to provide minimum wages to its workers and full health insurance for every Nike employee.

The textile industry can have damaging effects on the environment. Some TNCs including Nike are attempting to address environmental issues. Nike runs

Fig. 4.4.4: Child labour in an LEDC

a Reuse-A-Shoe scheme which recycles old shoes by grinding them up and making them into a surface for a sports field or playground. In addition, Nike uses some organic cotton, and has made a shoe from recycled material.

Positive effects

Globalisation does bring some benefits to LEDCs.

When TNCs come into a country, they provide jobs which, together with goods being shipped out of the country (exports), should increase the country's wealth. Workers may gain skills, practical and managerial, that they may not otherwise have had the opportunity to gain. They and their children may also benefit from healthcare and/or education schemes provided by the TNC.

Communities often benefit from an improved transport infrastructure, with new roads being built. Factories need energy so power supplies are improved. And, as one TNC moves in, others sometimes follow, thereby increasing the impact of these benefits.

The effect of globalisation on MEDCs

As manufacturing jobs move to LEDCs, manufacturing industries close down in MEDCs and employees suffer job losses. However, the advantage of globalisation is that companies can often supply a greater range of cheaper products to their markets while maintaining and indeed growing their profits.

Exercise 4D

1. (a) On a blank outline map of the world label, and shade in one colour, all the countries in which Nike has supplier factories.
   (b) Now label and shade in another colour those countries in which other TNCs have supplier factories. You may need to do some research on the internet or in your library.

2. Draw the Nike logo. Around the logo write labels describing what effect Nike is having on people in LEDCs. Include as many facts and figures as you can. Use the internet to help with your research.

3. Explain the meaning of each of the following terms:

   sweatshops   **labour intensive**

   regulations   **living wage**

4.   Investigate how and where any TNCs have exploited conditions in LEDCs and write up your findings.

5.   (a) Explain what actions Nike has taken to have a more positive effect in the LEDCs where it has supplier factories.
     (b) What other efforts do you think TNCs could make to have more positive effects in the LEDCs which supply their goods?

Extension question

6.   Explain which different groups in society you think are responsible for preventing exploitation of low wages and unregulated working conditions in LEDCs. Discuss measures those responsible could take to abolish these practices.

Glossary

Agriculture	The practice of farming, including the cultivation of the soil for the growing of crops and the rearing of animals to provide food, wool and other products.
Arable farming	The farming of crops in soil.
Assemble	Put parts together to make a product, e.g. cars on an assembly line.
Biodegrade	The process of an object being broken down naturally by nature.
Components	Pre-manufactured parts that are put together on an assembly line.
Distribution	The spread of an activity across a given area, e.g. farming types across Britain.
Diversification	The process of farmers using their land for activities other than farming, encouraged by government schemes such as set-aside.
Economy	The state of a country or region in terms of the production and consumption of goods and services and the supply of money.
Employment	The state of having paid work.
European Union (EU)	A group of 27 (as at 1st January 2011) European countries which have grouped together to make trade and aid easier for each other.
Extensive farming	The operation of farms that do not spend a lot of money on machinery and labour and are usually on a large scale e.g. sheep farms.
Fallow	Fields allowed to return to grass instead of being ploughed for growing crops.
Fertile	A term used to describe a soil that has many nutrients and therefore is very good for growing crops on, often found on the floodplains of rivers benefiting from alluvium deposits (silt).
Footloose	Industries that can locate in a variety of locations and are not tied down to one place by heavy or perishable raw materials.
Globalisation	The process of spreading company ideas and business around the world.

Grant	Money given by the government, e.g. to farmers, to promote production of a particular form of agricultural product such as milk.
Hi-tech goods	Lightweight telecommunications and computer equipment such as mobile phones and laptop computers.
Human factors	Those aspects of society, including location of the market and the intervention of government, which affect a farmer's decision about where to locate and the type of farming.
Industrial Revolution	A period of rapid mechanisation and prosperity in industry. People left the countryside to work in factories in towns and cities.
Industries	Economic activity concerned with the processing of raw materials and the manufacture of goods in factories.
Infrastructure	Basic but essential communications and services such as schools, hospitals, roads, water and electricity supply.
Intensive farming	Farming with the aim of achieving maximum production within a limited area, especially by using chemicals and machines.
Labour	People who work.
Labour intensive	Requiring lots of labour (e.g. textile manufacturing).
LEDC	Less Economically Developed Country.
Living wage	A wage that will give an employee enough money for food and housing.
Location factor	A reason why an industry may choose to be located in a certain place.
Manufacture	To make products such as cars, furniture and electrical items from raw materials.
Market gardening	Growing of fruit and vegetables in controlled greenhouse conditions.
MEDC	More Economically Developed Country.
Mixed farming	The use of a single farm for multiple purposes, e.g. arable and pastoral farming.
National grid	National network for supplying electricity.

Noise pollution	Pollution caused by noise from air and car traffic, nightclubs, building sites, quarries etc.
Package holidays	Holidays that include the flight, hotel or self-catering accommodation and the help of a resort representative.
Pastoral farming	The rearing of animals.
Perishable goods	Goods that will go bad in a short period of time such as fruit and vegetables.
Pesticides	Chemicals sprayed on crops to kill insects that could damage the crop.
Physical factors	Natural influences such as the weather or relief on the location of an activity such as farming.
Primary activities	Taking raw materials from the land and the sea. These tend to be very large and old industries such as farming, fishing, mining and forestry.
Quaternary activities	Research and development of new ideas and goods in areas such as medicine and computer technology.
Quota	A set amount of produce a farmer may sell, for example in the European Union.
Raw materials	Resources such as coal that are taken from the ground during primary activities.
Regulation	Rules applied by companies or governments.
Science park	A specially built environment for high-tech industries which typically have links with a local university.
Seasonal jobs	Jobs that are only for a short time (a season) such as picking fruit in the summer on fruit farms or working in a chalet during the ski season.
Secondary activities	Industries that manufacture or process the raw material collected in a primary industry, such as food processing, car assembly and oil refining.
Service	A provision for the public, such as shops, financial services, education, police and health services.

Subsidy	Financial assistance given to farmers to help them stay in business and remain profitable.
Subsistence agriculture	Growing crops or rearing animals for one's own consumption and not for sale to a secondary industry.
Surplus	Spare food created from agricultural overproduction.
Sweatshops	Factories in LEDCs that pack many workers into a small space, often with little ventilation or fresh water supply.
Technological revolution	Recent period of history which has seen the rapid development of lightweight telecommunications and computer equipment.
Tertiary activities	Industries that are involved in selling (retailing) such as supermarkets and department stores, as well as all industries providing services such as entertainment, finance, health and education.
Textile industry	The manufacturing of clothes and fabrics.
Tourism	When people visit and stay in destinations in the UK and abroad, for reasons including recreation.
Transnational corporation (TNC)	A company that has different parts of its company or company branches in different countries, often exploiting cheap labour in LEDCs.
Urban	A built-up, settled area, typically of houses and/or flats.
Visual pollution	Ugly buildings that spoil the natural beauty of the landscape.

Chapter 5: Location knowledge

In this chapter we will look at:

- The names and locations of the world's continents, oceans and other major physical features, such as mountain ranges, deserts and river basins.

- The meaning of latitude and longitude, and how these imaginary lines play an important role in geography.

- The physical geography of the British Isles, focusing on the borders between the countries of the British Isles, as well as identifying the capital cities, major mountain ranges and rivers.

- Countries that are members of the European Union and what it means to be a member.

- A few other interesting countries.

5.1 Where in the world?

Continents and oceans

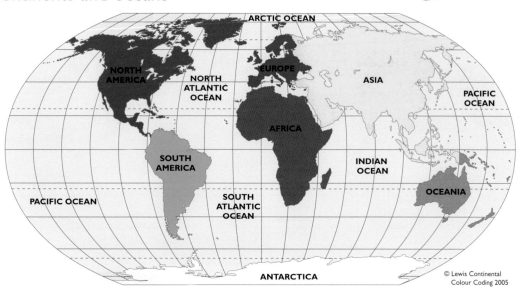

Fig. 5.1.1: Continents and oceans

The location of the world's **continents** and oceans are shown on Fig. 5.1.1. Make sure you can label the oceans and continents. Here are some other important things to remember:

- The continent of North America includes the countries of the USA, Canada and Mexico, not just the USA.

- Oceania is the name given to the region that includes the countries of Australia, New Zealand, Papua New Guinea and the many islands in the Pacific Ocean.

- The ocean that divides North America and Europe is the North Atlantic Ocean.

- The Arctic Ocean surrounds the North Pole.

- The Southern Ocean surrounds the continent of Antarctica and the South Pole.

- The world's largest ocean, the Pacific Ocean divides the Americas in the east and Australia and Asia in the west.

- The Indian Ocean is bound by Asia in the north, Africa in the west and Indonesia and Australia in the east.

Mountain ranges and deserts

There are five major mountain ranges across the world which you need to be able to name, locate and plot on a map. Make sure that you can:

- plot a mountain range on a base map

- name a mountain range that is labelled with a letter on a map.

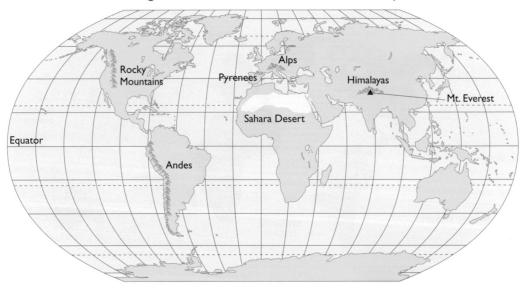

Fig. 5.1.2: Mountain ranges and deserts

The location of the five major mountain ranges and one **desert** area is shown on Fig. 5.1.2:

- The Sahara Desert in Northern Africa (see Fig. 5.1.3) is the world's largest hot desert, covering an approximate area of 9 million square kilometres (3.5 million square miles). The name 'Sahara' means desert in Arabic.

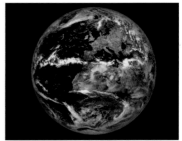

Fig. 5.1.3: Satellite image of the Sahara Desert

The five major mountain ranges are:

- The Alps, which stretch across eastern France, northern Italy, Switzerland and Austria.

- The Pyrenees, which cover the border between southern France and northern Spain.

- The Rocky Mountains, which are located in western Canada and western and central USA.

- The Andes, which stretch in a continuous line all along the west coast of South America. There are volcanoes among the mountains.

- The Himalayas, the largest and highest range of mountains, which is located in Asia. Formed by the meeting of two of the Earth's giant tectonic plates, the Himalayas are home to the world's highest mountain, Mount Everest at 8850 m (see Fig. 5.1.4).

Fig. 5.1.4: Mount Everest in the Himalayas

Major river basins

A **river basin** is an area of land which is drained by a river and its **tributaries**. There are many large river basins in the world, providing a valuable resource for both wildlife and people. There are five of these that it is particularly important to know (see Fig. 5.1.5.

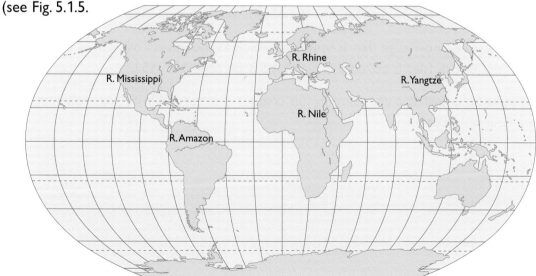

Fig. 5.1.5: Major river basins

- The Amazon river basin in *South America* has its source in the Andes and covers much of Brazil. It is the largest river basin in the world, covering an area of 6,915,000 square kilometres (2,670,000 square miles). The Amazon is the world's largest river by volume (see Fig. 5.1.6).

Fig. 5.1.6: The Amazon

- The Nile is 6690 kilometres (4157 miles) long and its tributaries flow through nine different countries (Uganda, Sudan, Egypt, Ethiopia, Zaire, Kenya, Tanzania, Rwanda and Burundi) before meeting the Mediterranean Sea at the Egyptian coast. It is thought by many to be the longest river in the world. However, in 2007 Brazil claimed to have discovered that the Amazon is longer than the Nile, and the debate continues.

- The Mississippi river basin covers over one third of the USA and has over 100 tributaries.

- The largest river in Asia is the Yangtze which flows from the northern Himalayas through China into the East China Sea.

- One of the most important rivers in northern Europe, providing **irrigation** for farmland, is the Rhine. With sources in the Alps, the Rhine either flows through or borders Switzerland, Liechtenstein, Austria, Germany, France and the Netherlands, before flowing into the North Sea at Rotterdam.

Other location knowledge that is important, such as mountains, hill ranges and rivers within the British Isles is covered in section 5.3 on page 146–151.

The location knowledge you learn in this chapter is extended in *So you really want to learn Geography Book 2*.

Exercise 5A

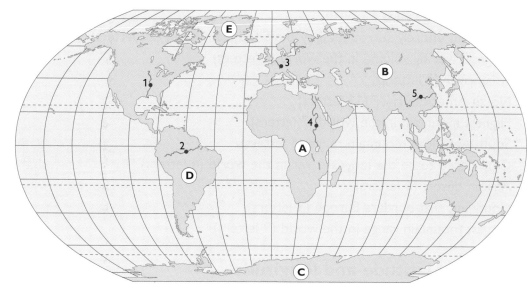

Fig. 5.1.7: Test map

1. (a) Name the continents marked A, B and C on the map in Fig. 5.1.7.
   (b) Which letter, D or E, is the odd one out? Why?

2. (a) Which ocean separates Europe and North America?
   (b) Which ocean separates Africa and Oceana?

3. (a) Which mountain range provides the source for the River Yangtze?
   (b) In which continent are these mountains?
   (c) What is the name of the highest mountain in this range?

4. (a) Which of the rivers marked (with numbers) on the map above is the Mississippi?
   (b) Which of the rivers marked is the Rhine?
   (c) Which is the largest river by volume in the world? What number is it on the map above?

5. (a) In which continent would you find the Sahara Desert?
   (b) What is the name of the river generally considered to be the longest in the world, which you can also find in this continent?

Exercise 5B

Solve the following clues.

1. Continent entirely surrounded by the Southern Ocean (10 letters)
2. Largest river by volume in the world (6 letters)
3. Asian river (7 letters)
4. North American river (11 letters)
5. Highest mountain in the world (7 letters)
6. South American mountain range (5 letters)
7. Considered to be the longest river in the world (4 letters)
8. African desert (6 letters)
9. Continent that borders Europe (4 letters)
10. Largest mountain range in the world (9 letters)

5.2 Lines of latitude and longitude

Lines of latitude

From your maths lessons you know that there are 360 degrees in a circle. Let us imagine a circular protractor placed over a sketch of the globe.

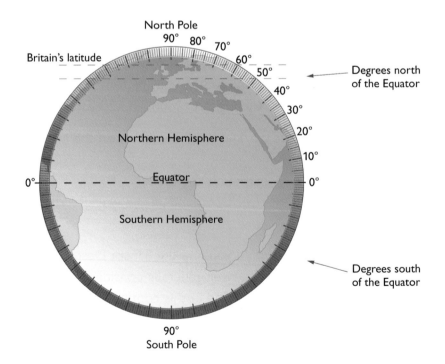

Fig. 5.2.1: The globe covered by a circular protractor

The globe can be divided up by imaginary lines that match the degrees of the protractor. These lines help us to describe the location of places more easily.

Lines of **latitude** are the imaginary lines that run horizontally, east to west around the globe and show how far north or south a location is. The line of latitude that runs around the centre of the globe is called the **Equator** and is given a value of 0°. It is the mid point between the North and South Poles and separates the **Northern Hemisphere** to the north and the **Southern Hemisphere** to the south. A latitude measurement, therefore, gives us a location which is north or south of the Equator. Latitudes increase from 0° at the Equator to 90° at either pole. The North Pole is 90° north and the South Pole is 90° south. The British Isles are located in the Northern Hemisphere, between 50° to 60° north (see Fig. 5.2.1).

The climate changes gradually over latitudes and, to some degree, we find the climate reflected in the same latitudes either side of the Equator, although of course factors other than latitude help create the climate in different locations.

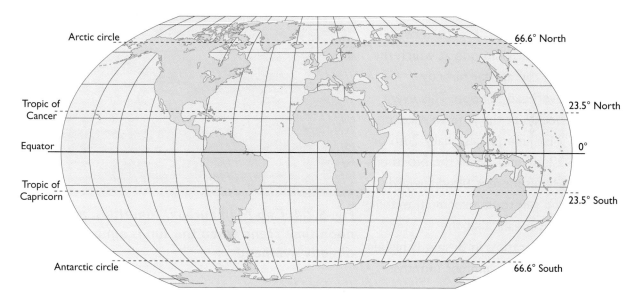

Fig. 5.2.2: Important lines of latitude

The tropics

The geographical region of the Earth centred on the Equator and called the tropics or the tropical zone is limited in latitude by the **Tropic of Cancer** and the **Tropic of Capricorn** (see Fig. 5.2.2). These lines of latitude have significance because they mirror the angle that the Earth tilts on its axis as it spins, giving us day and night.

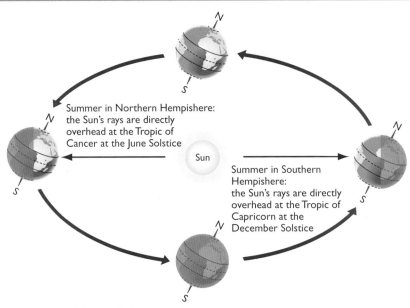

Fig 5.2.3: How the tilting of the Earth gives us the seasons

Fig. 5.2.4: Cap Malheureux, Mauritius: a noon time scene when the sun is almost directly overhead

- The Tropic of Cancer is at 23.3° north in the Northern Hemisphere. It is the most northerly latitude at which the sun can appear directly overhead at noon. This event occurs at the June solstice, on 21st June (occasionally 20th or 22nd June), when the Northern Hemisphere is tilted towards the sun to its maximum extent. This means that the temperature in Britain is higher during the summer months.

- The Tropic of Capricorn is at 23.3° south in the Southern Hemisphere. It is the most southerly latitude at which the sun can appear directly overhead at noon. This event occurs at the December solstice, on the 21st December (occasionally 22nd December) when the Southern Hemisphere is tilted towards the sun to its maximum extent. At this time, the Southern Hemisphere experiences summer and the Northern Hemisphere experiences winter.

The polar regions

The further from the Equator we travel, either north or south, the colder it gets because the Earth is tilted further away from the sun. Thus at 66.6° north we find the **Arctic Circle** and at 66.6° south we find the **Antarctic Circle** (see Fig. 5.2.2).

Lines of longitude

Just as the earth can be split up horizontally by imaginary lines of latitude, it can also be split up vertically by lines of **longitude,** from the North Pole to the South Pole, to show how far east and west places are. These lines of longitude create the Eastern and Western Hemispheres, separated by the Prime Meridian (see Fig. 5.2.5).

The Prime Meridian

The line of longitude which is given the value of 0° (like the Equator) is the **Greenwich Meridian** or **Prime Meridian**. This line runs from the North Pole through London to the South Pole. Anywhere east of the Prime Meridian will have a longitude value between 0° and 180° east. For example, Cairo is just over 30° east. Anywhere west of the Prime Meridian will have a longitude value of somewhere between 0° and 180° west. For example, New York is just over 75° west.

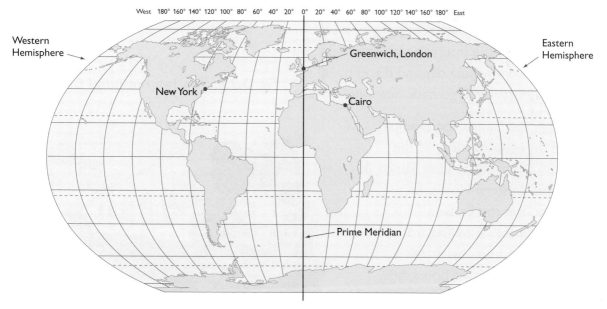

Fig. 5.2.5: The Prime Meridian

The International Date Line

The **International Date Line** runs from pole to pole, down the opposite side of the globe to the Prime Meridian, on the 180° line of longitude, in the middle of the Pacific Ocean (see Fig. 5.2.6). It is the imaginary line that separates two consecutive calendar days. The date to the left of this line (i.e. in the Eastern Hemisphere) is always one day ahead of the date to the right of this line (in the Western Hemisphere).

Unlike all the other lines of latitude and longitude, the International Date Line is not a perfectly straight line and deliberately avoids populated landmasses. It has also been moved slightly over the years to accommodate the needs of various countries in the Pacific Ocean. Longitude has a very important influence on human life, as it defines time zones. If you travel west across the International Date Line you advance one whole day and if you travel east across it you go back one whole day.

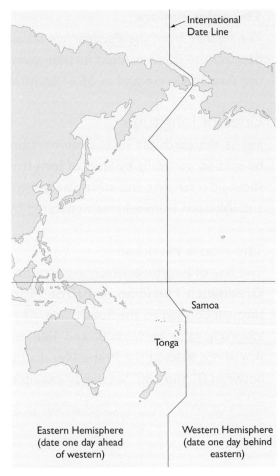

International Date Line

Samoa

Tonga

Eastern Hemisphere
(date one day ahead
of western)

Western Hemisphere
(date one day behind
eastern)

Fig. 5.2.6: The International Date Line

Tonga and Samoa, for example, are on opposite sides of the International Date Line: Samoa is in the Western Hemisphere; Tonga is in the Eastern Hemisphere. Travelling from Tonga to Samoa by air takes approximately two hours, but involves crossing the International Date Line so the time difference is 24 hours. Passengers arrive the day before they left!

Exercise 5C

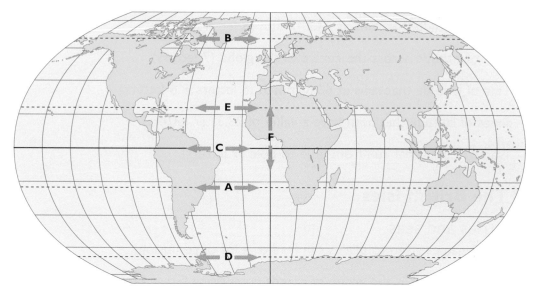

Fig. 5.2.7: Test map

1. Look at the map in Fig. 5.2.7. Name the lines of latitude identified by the letters A to E.

2. (a) What are the values in degrees of the Tropic of Cancer and the Tropic of Capricorn?
   (b) How does latitude relate to changes in climate across the globe?

3. (a) Name the line of longitude marked with the letter F on the map above.
   (b) What is the value in degrees of this line of longitude?

4. Use an atlas to identify the approximate latitude and longitude of one major city in Europe, Asia, Oceania, North America and South America.

5. Explain why the International Date Line is not a straight line like all the other lines of longitude and latitude.

Exercise 5D

Solve the following clues.

1. Name of lines that run horizontally across the globe (8 letters)

2. Half of the globe (10 letters)

3. Value in degrees of each pole (north or south) (6 letters)

4. Line of latitude that runs at 23.3 degrees north (6 letters)

5. Value in degrees of the Equator (4 letters)

6. Line of latitude that runs at 23.3° south (9 letters)

7. Line of latitude across the centre of the globe (7 letters)

8. Line of latitude that runs at 66.6° north (5 letters + 6 letters)

9. Lines of latitude that both have a value of 23.3° (7 letters)

10. Name of lines that run from pole to pole (9 letters)

5.3 The British Isles

Countries and seas

Sometimes names given to places can lead to a lot of confusion!

- The British Isles is the group of islands comprising Great Britain, the whole of Ireland and a number of smaller islands such as the Isle of Man (see Fig. 5.3.1).

- Great Britain is the largest island within the British Isles (and in fact within Europe). Great Britain incorporates the countries of England, Scotland and Wales (see Fig. 5.3.2).

- The United Kingdom is the term used to describe the four countries that are governed by Parliament in London: England, Wales, Scotland and Northern Ireland. However, in 1999 the UK devolution created the Scottish Parliament, the National Assembly of Wales and the Northern Ireland Assembly, giving these countries certain powers over themselves. The United Kingdom does not include the Republic of Ireland (Eire),

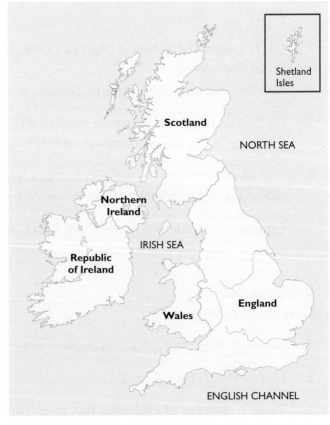

Fig. 5.3.1: The British Isles

which is a separate country, nor the Isle of Man or the Channel Islands, which are self-governing crown dependencies (British possessions that are not part of the United Kingdom and have their own system of government, see Fig. 5.3.3).

Fig. 5.3.2: Great Britain   **Fig. 5.3.3: The United Kingdom**

The three sea areas that surround the British Isles are identified on Fig. 5.3.1.

●   The Irish Sea divides Ireland and Great Britain and is connected to the Atlantic Ocean to the north and south.

●   The English Channel is the 562 km (21 miles) long (from its western point to its eastern point) stretch of water that divides England and France. The channel widens to the west where it meets the Atlantic Ocean but narrows to just 34 km (21 miles) wide to the east, where it runs between the ports of Dover in England and Calais on the French coast (see Fig. 5.3.4).

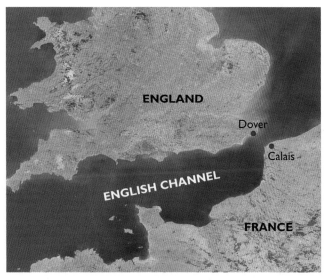

Fig. 5.3.4: Satellite image of the English Channel

- The North Sea is by far the largest sea area that borders the British Isles. It separates Britain from the coastlines of the northern European countries of the Netherlands and Germany, as well as the Scandinavian countries of Denmark, Norway and Sweden.

Rivers

Rivers have been vital to farmers, settlements and industry in Britain throughout history. The three major rivers in Great Britain are the River Severn, the River Thames and the River Trent (see Fig. 5.3.5). If you are taking CE then you should ensure you can recognise and sketch the course of these rivers.

- The River Severn is Britain's longest river, stretching some 354 km (220 miles) from its source in the Welsh mountains to its mouth in the Bristol Channel (see Fig. 5.3.6). The River Severn flows into the Atlantic Ocean.

- The River Thames is probably Britain's most well known river, flowing through London before discharging into the North Sea. It is the second longest river in Britain.

- The River Trent is a large river that flows from its source in Staffordshire through the Midlands towards the north-east. It joins the Humber Estuary before flowing into the North Sea.

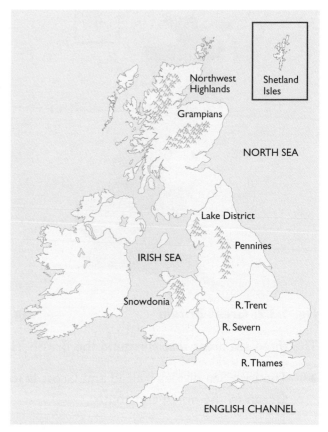

Fig. 5.3.5: Rivers and hills/mountains in Great Britain

Fig. 5.3.6: The River Severn at Shrewsbury

Hills and mountain ranges

Great Britain has several chains of hills or mountains which are often partly or wholly designated **National Parks**. For example, Snowdonia National Park covers, among others, the Snowdon range in North Wales, and the Peak District National Park covers part of the Pennines. If you are taking CE make sure you can locate the following hills and mountain ranges on a map of Great Britain (see Fig. 5.3.5):

- The Northwest Highlands are a range of mountains located in the very north of Scotland.

- The Grampians stretch from the west coast to the east coast of Scotland and contain the highest mountain in Britain, Ben Nevis, which is 1344 metres (4409 feet) above sea level (see Fig. 5.3.7).

Fig. 5.3.7: Ben Nevis in the Grampian mountains

- The Pennines are a range of mountains that divide northern Britain into east and west. They stretch some 402 km (250 miles) from the Scottish border in the north to the Peak District in the Midlands and are often called the backbone of Britain.

- The Lake District is a region of mountains and lakes. The highest mountain in the Lake District is Scafell Pike, which stands at 978 metres (3209 feet).

- Snowdonia is a mountain range in North Wales, with its highest peak at 1085 metres (3560 feet).

Capital cities of the British Isles

Each country in the British Isles has a capital city. If you are taking CE it is important that you can recognise these capital cities and plot their locations on a map (see Fig. 5.3.8).

- London is the capital city of England and of the United Kingdom as a whole. The city was first settled over 2000 years ago and has a population of around 8 million people. It is now a major world city renowned for its business, history and tourist attractions.

- Edinburgh is the capital city of Scotland and is built around an extinct volcano, upon which Edinburgh Castle was built. Edinburgh is on the River Forth and is located on the east coast of Scotland, between the Southern Uplands and the Grampian mountains.

Fig. 5.3.8: Capital cities of the United Kingdom and the capital of the Republic of Ireland

- Cardiff is the capital city of Wales. Unlike London or Edinburgh, Cardiff was a small settlement until its rapid growth in the 19th and 20th centuries when it became a major port. Cardiff lies on the south coast of Wales facing the Bristol Channel.

- Belfast is the capital city of Northern Ireland. The city straddles the border of County Antrim and County Down and is located on Northern Ireland's east coast, facing the Irish sea.

- Dublin is the capital city of the Republic of Ireland (Eire).

Other useful things to know

You will learn about other important cities and National Parks in the British Isles and other rivers in the Republic of Ireland and Scotland in the next book in this series, *So you really want to learn Geography Book 2.*

Exercise 5E

Study the map in Fig. 5.3.9 and answer the following questions:

1. (a) Name the two major islands that make up the British Isles.
    (b) Name the four countries that make up the United Kingdom.

2. (a) Which is the correct border between England and Scotland: line 1, 2 or 3?
    (b) What is the name of the capital city marked C? Which country is it in?

3. (a) What is the name of the sea marked A?
    (b) What is the name of the sea marked B?
    (c) From which group of countries does the North Sea separate the British Isles?

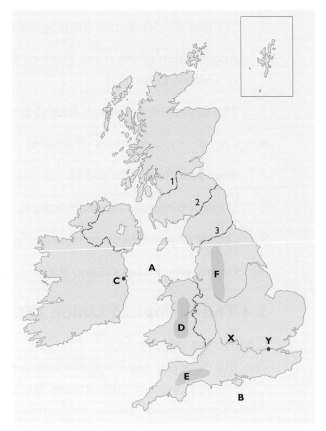

Fig. 5.3.9: Test map

4. (a) Name the river marked X on the map and the city that it flows through, marked Y.
    (b) Into which sea does this river flow?

5. (a) Name the two main mountain ranges in Scotland.
    (b) Are the Pennines located in area D, E or F?

Exercise 5F

Solve the following clues.

1. Capital city of Wales (7 letters)

2. River that flows into the Bristol Channel (6 letters)

3. Sea that divides Britain from Scandinavia (5 letters)

4. Abbreviation of the name given to England, Scotland, Wales and Northern Ireland as a whole (2 letters)

5. The largest of the British Isles (5 letters + 7 letters)

6. Capital city of Scotland (9 letters)

7. River that flows into the North Sea (5 letters)

8. Scottish mountain range (9 letters)

9. Capital city of Northern Ireland (7 letters)

10. Capital city of England and the United Kingdom (6 letters)

5.4 The European Union (EU)

Countries of the EU

The **EU** (formerly the European Economic Community) owes its origin to the Treaty of Rome signed in 1957 by the six founding countries: Germany, France, Italy, Belgium, Luxembourg and The Netherlands. The UK joined in 1973.

In 1992 the Treaty of Maastricht established the title European Union and significantly extended the EU from a free trade area, to create a single market governed by a system of EU laws. The headquarters are in Brussels, the capital of Belgium (see Fig. 5.4.1).

Within the EU people, goods, services and capital can move freely. The EU also maintains a common trade policy, agricultural and fisheries policies, and

Fig. 5.4.1: The EU Parliament in Brussels

a regional development policy. In 1999 the EU introduced a common currency, the **euro** (€), which by 2011 had been adopted by 17 member states (see Fig. 5.4.2).

As at 1st January 2011 there were 27 European member countries of the EU, but it is important to remember that other European countries may join in the future.

Fig. 5.4.2: The euro (€)

Most, but not all, European countries are members of the EU: Switzerland and Norway have chosen not to join because they felt that the economic advantages would not outweigh the disadvantages. In recent years, less wealthy developed countries have been allowed to join the EU: Romania and Bulgaria were given membership in early 2007. The Ukraine (which was formerly a member of the Soviet Union) is a large and relatively poor county bordering the EU group of countries, but it is not yet a member of the EU. Residents of European countries are permitted to live and work in any other European country. This freedom, combined with considerably higher wages in northern European countries such as Britain, has led to increased **migration**.

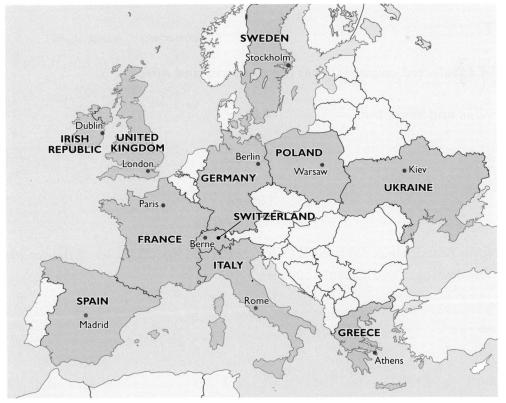

Fig. 5.4.3: European countries and their capitals that you should know for CE

5.5 Other countries

Much of what you are expected to know is based on European geography. However, for CE you will be tested on the location of other countries across the globe. Fig. 5.4.4 identifies nine different countries taken from three continents: North America, South America and Africa, that you should know for CE.

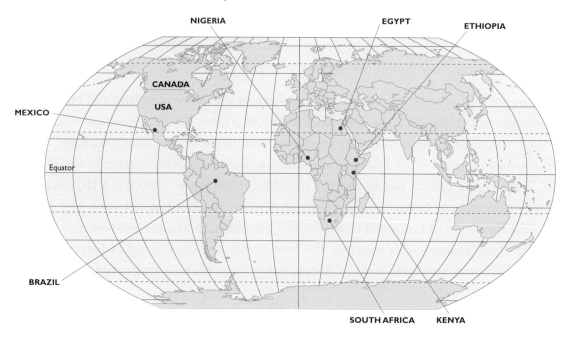

Fig. 5.4.4: Selected countries from the Americas and Africa

Americas and West Indies
Brazil
Canada
Mexico
USA

Africa
Egypt
Ethiopia
Kenya
Nigeria
South Africa

● North America includes two MEDCs: Canada and the USA, two of the world's most developed and affluent countries.

- Central and South America contains LEDCs and is generally composed of less developed countries and NICs such as Brazil. These countries have high urban populations, often with shanty town settlements on the outskirts of their major cities (see Fig. 5.4.5).

- Africa is home to some of the poorest countries in the world. This is due to a number of reasons, both political and geographical. Other countries in Africa are wealthy and influential. Egypt and Kenya, for example, have increased their wealth by developing tourism, while South Africa has maximised its natural resources.

Fig. 5.4.5: A shanty town on the outskirts of Sao Paulo, Brazil, in South America

Fig. 5.4.6 identifies different countries in two other continents: Asia and Oceania.

Asia

		Oceania
Afghanistan	Russia	Australia
Bangladesh	Saudi Arabia	New Zealand
China		
India		
Indonesia		
Iran		
Iraq		

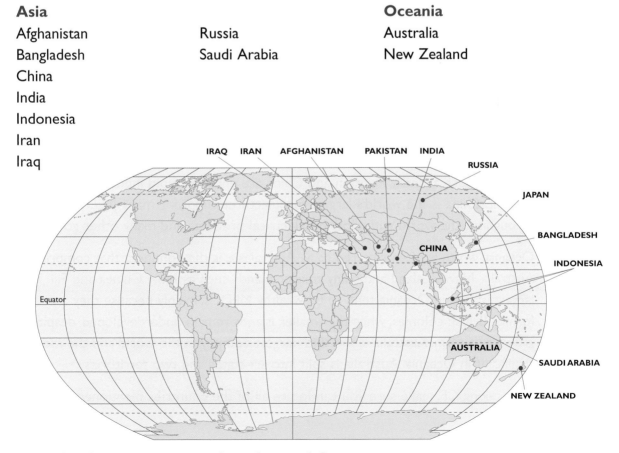

Fig. 5.4.6: Selected countries from Asia and Oceania

- Asia is the world's largest and most populous continent. It covers 8.6% of the Earth's total surface area (or 29.4% of its land area) and, with almost 4 billion people, it contains more than 60% of the world's current population. Many of the cities in Asia have among the highest population totals and densities in the world.

Fig. 5.4.7: Many Asian cities have very high population densities

Although relatively poor compared to the wealthy countries of Europe, Asian countries such as India, Pakistan and China are enjoying rapid industrial growth at present. China is the world's largest manufacturer, supplying many MEDCs throughout the world with clothing, electrical products and many other goods.

- Oceania, which is often referred to as Australasia, is the continent that comprises Australia, New Zealand and many smaller islands such as New Guinea and Fiji. The largest islands in Oceania tend to be wealthy MEDCs, mainly because they are former British colonies, while the smaller islands remain underdeveloped, despite growing tourism. Australia is the sixth largest country in the world and the most significant in Oceania. Australia is split into six states and two territories.

If you are taking CE, make sure you can locate all of the countries mentioned in this section.

Exercise 5G

Study Fig. 5.4.8 and answer the questions that follow.

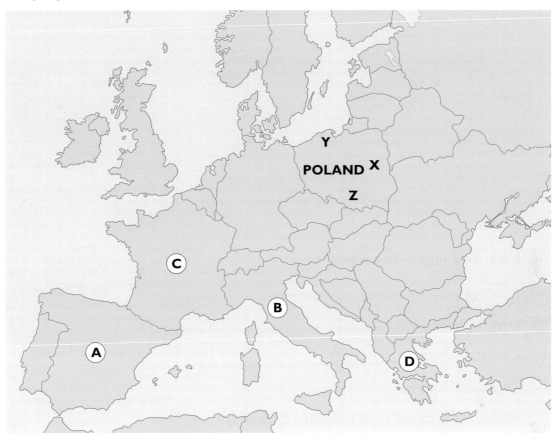

Fig. 5.4.8: Test map – Europe

1. (a) Name the European countries marked A to D on the map above.
   (b) Name the capital cities of these countries.

2. (a) What is the capital of Poland?
   (b) Which letter (X, Y or Z) on the map above is the correct location of Poland's capital?

Now study Fig. 5.4.9.

3. Name the countries marked A to E.

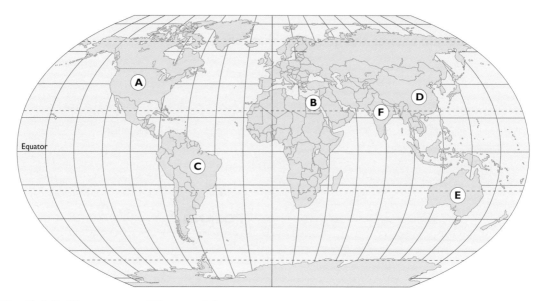

Fig. 5.4.9: Test map – The world

Exercise 5H

Solve the following clues.

1. Capital of Germany (6 letters)

2. Capital of Greece (6 letters)

3. Madrid is the capital of this country (5 letters)

4. Eastern European country beginning with the letter U (7 letters)

5. Capital of the Republic of Ireland (5 letters)

6. European country with Warsaw as its capital (6 letters)

7. Low-lying Asian country (10 letters)

8. Non-EU member in Europe (11 letters)

9. Capital of Italy (4 letters)

10. European country with Stockholm as its capital (6 letters)

End of chapter activity

This game can be played at home or at school. With the help of a parent or teacher enlarge copies of a map of the world and a map of Europe, which have the country borders on them but are not labelled with the names (available for download from the Galore Park website, www.galorepark.co.uk). Use a coloured pencil to colour in the countries you need to know for the CE exam. Make 20 small paper balls and share them between you. You are now ready to begin the game.

1. Challenge your partner to throw a paper ball to land on a particular country (one of those that you need to know for the CE exam).

2. If the ball lands on the country they get three points, plus a bonus point if they can name the capital.

3. If they don't land on the country you named, but landed on another country that has colour on it, they can earn a point by naming that country, plus a bonus point if they can name the capital.

4. Now it is your partner's turn to challenge you!

5. Keep a record of how many points you each score. See who has won after throwing ten paper balls each.

Good luck and see you again in *So you really want to learn Geography Book 2.*

Glossary

Antarctic Circle	The line of latitude 66.6 degrees south of the Equator.
Arctic Circle	The line of latitude 66.6 degrees north of the Equator.
Continent	A large land mass.
Desert	A hot or cold region of barren land.
Equator	The imaginary line running round the middle of the Earth.
Euro	The common currency used by 17 of the 27 EU countries.
European Union (EU)	A group of 27 European countries that have grouped together to make trade and aid easier for each other.
International Date Line	The line of longitude running from pole to pole in the opposite direction to the Greenwich Meridian.
Irrigation	Artificial watering of the land.
Latitude	The distance north or south of the Equator.
Longitude	The distance east or west of the Prime Meridian.
Migration	The movement of people from one area to another seeking work, health and social benefits.
National Park	An area of countryside of outstanding beauty which is protected from development.
Northern Hemisphere	The area to the north of the Equator.
Prime Meridian/ Greenwich Meridian	The line of longitude running from pole to pole through Greenwich in London.
River basin	The catchment area drained by a river.
Southern Hemisphere	The area to the south of the Equator.
Tributary	A river joining a larger river.
Tropic of Cancer	The line of latitude 23.5 degrees north of the Equator.
Tropic of Capricorn	The line of latitude 23.5 degrees south of the Equator.

Appendix 1: Ordnance Survey map keys

Key taken from 1:25 000 Scale OS Explorer maps

Ordnance Survey®

Explorer™ series (1:25 000 scale)

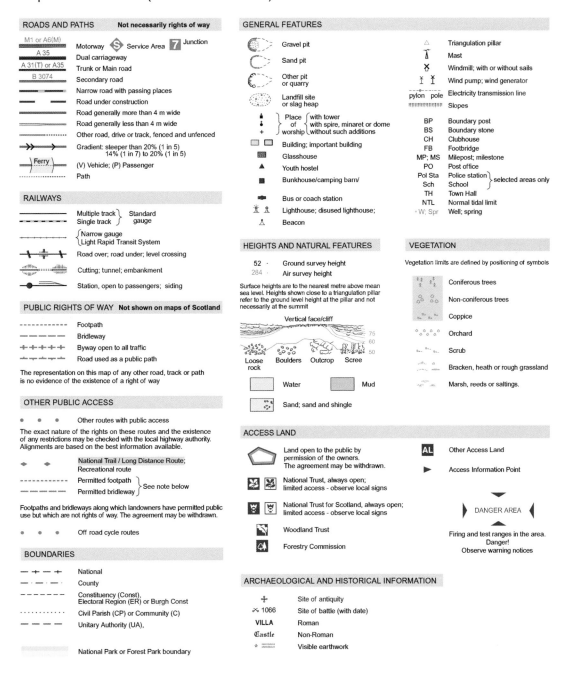

ROADS AND PATHS — Not necessarily rights of way

M1 or A6(M)	Motorway — Service Area — Junction
A 35	Dual carriageway
A 31(T) or A35	Trunk or Main road
B 3074	Secondary road
	Narrow road with passing places
	Road under construction
	Road generally more than 4 m wide
	Road generally less than 4 m wide
	Other road, drive or track, fenced and unfenced
	Gradient: steeper than 20% (1 in 5) 14% (1 in 7) to 20% (1 in 5)
Ferry	(V) Vehicle; (P) Passenger
	Path

RAILWAYS

- Multiple track / Single track } Standard gauge
- Narrow gauge / Light Rapid Transit System
- Road over; road under; level crossing
- Cutting; tunnel; embankment
- Station, open to passengers; siding

PUBLIC RIGHTS OF WAY — Not shown on maps of Scotland

- Footpath
- Bridleway
- +++++ Byway open to all traffic
- Road used as a public path

The representation on this map of any other road, track or path is no evidence of the existence of a right of way

OTHER PUBLIC ACCESS

- • • • Other routes with public access

The exact nature of the rights on these routes and the existence of any restrictions may be checked with the local highway authority. Alignments are based on the best information available.

- National Trail / Long Distance Route; Recreational route
- Permitted footpath } See note below
- Permitted bridleway }

Footpaths and bridleways along which landowners have permitted public use but which are not rights of way. The agreement may be withdrawn.

- • • • Off road cycle routes

BOUNDARIES

- — + — + National
- — · — · County
- — — — — Constituency (Const), Electoral Region (ER) or Burgh Const
- · · · · · · Civil Parish (CP) or Community (C)
- — — — Unitary Authority (UA),
- National Park or Forest Park boundary

GENERAL FEATURES

	Gravel pit
	Sand pit
	Other pit or quarry
	Landfill site or slag heap
	Place of worship { with tower / with spire, minaret or dome / without such additions }
	Building; important building
	Glasshouse
▲	Youth hostel
■	Bunkhouse/camping barn/
	Bus or coach station
	Lighthouse; disused lighthouse;
	Beacon

△	Triangulation pillar
	Mast
	Windmill; with or without sails
	Wind pump; wind generator
pylon pole	Electricity transmission line
	Slopes
BP	Boundary post
BS	Boundary stone
CH	Clubhouse
FB	Footbridge
MP; MS	Milepost; milestone
PO	Post office
Pol Sta	Police station } selected areas only
Sch	School
TH	Town Hall
NTL	Normal tidal limit
· W; Spr	Well; spring

HEIGHTS AND NATURAL FEATURES

- 52 · Ground survey height
- 284 · Air survey height

Surface heights are to the nearest metre above mean sea level. Heights shown close to a triangulation pillar refer to the ground level height at the pillar and not necessarily at the summit

Vertical face/cliff

Loose rock — Boulders — Outcrop — Scree

- Water
- Mud
- Sand; sand and shingle

ACCESS LAND

- Land open to the public by permission of the owners. The agreement may be withdrawn.
- National Trust, always open; limited access - observe local signs
- National Trust for Scotland, always open; limited access - observe local signs
- Woodland Trust
- Forestry Commission

- AL — Other Access Land
- ► — Access Information Point

DANGER AREA

Firing and test ranges in the area. Danger! Observe warning notices

VEGETATION

Vegetation limits are defined by positioning of symbols

- Coniferous trees
- Non-coniferous trees
- Coppice
- Orchard
- Scrub
- Bracken, heath or rough grassland
- Marsh, reeds or saltings.

ARCHAEOLOGICAL AND HISTORICAL INFORMATION

✠	Site of antiquity
⚔ 1066	Site of battle (with date)
VILLA	Roman
Castle	Non-Roman
☆	Visible earthwork

Key taken from 1:25 000 Scale OS Explorer maps (continued)

Explorer™ series (1:25 000 scale)

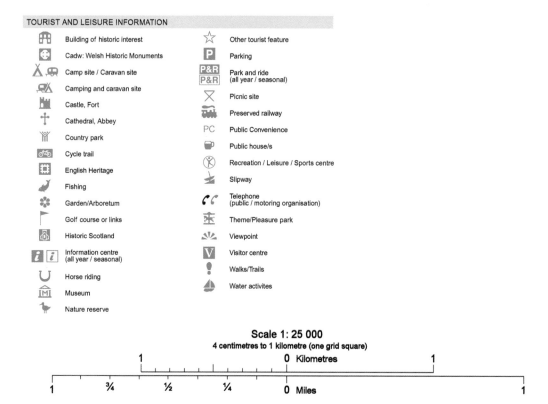

Scale 1: 25 000
4 centimetres to 1 kilometre (one grid square)

NB. Due to changes in specification there are differences on some sheets

Key taken from 1:50 000 Scale OS Landranger maps

OS Landranger® (1:50 000 scale)

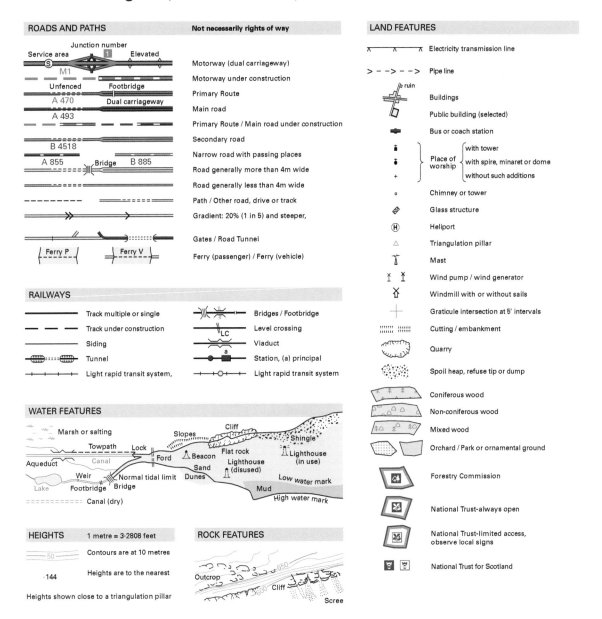

ROADS AND PATHS

Not necessarily rights of way

Motorway (dual carriageway)
Motorway under construction
Primary Route
Main road
Primary Route / Main road under construction
Secondary road
Narrow road with passing places
Road generally more than 4m wide
Road generally less than 4m wide
Path / Other road, drive or track
Gradient: 20% (1 in 5) and steeper,
Gates / Road Tunnel
Ferry (passenger) / Ferry (vehicle)

RAILWAYS

Track multiple or single
Track under construction
Siding
Tunnel
Light rapid transit system,

Bridges / Footbridge
Level crossing
Viaduct
Station, (a) principal
Light rapid transit system

WATER FEATURES

Marsh or salting
Towpath Lock
Aqueduct Canal
Weir
Lake Footbridge Bridge
Slopes Cliff
Shingle
Flat rock
Beacon Lighthouse Lighthouse
Sand (disused) (in use)
Dunes
Normal tidal limit
Low water mark
Mud
High water mark
Canal (dry)

HEIGHTS

1 metre = 3·2808 feet
Contours are at 10 metres
·144 Heights are to the nearest
Heights shown close to a triangulation pillar

ROCK FEATURES

Outcrop
Cliff
Scree

LAND FEATURES

Electricity transmission line
Pipe line
Buildings
Public building (selected)
Bus or coach station
Place of worship { with tower / with spire, minaret or dome / without such additions }
Chimney or tower
Glass structure
Heliport
Triangulation pillar
Mast
Wind pump / wind generator
Windmill with or without sails
Graticule intersection at 5' intervals
Cutting / embankment
Quarry
Spoil heap, refuse tip or dump
Coniferous wood
Non-coniferous wood
Mixed wood
Orchard / Park or ornamental ground
Forestry Commission
National Trust-always open
National Trust-limited access, observe local signs
National Trust for Scotland

Key taken from 1:50 000 Scale OS Landranger maps (continued)

 Ordnance Survey®

OS Landranger® (1:50 000 scale)

PUBLIC RIGHTS OF WAY

....	Footpath
– – – – – – –	Bridleway
–·–·–·–·–·	Road used as a public path
–+–+–+–+–+	Byway open to all traffic

The symbols show the defined route so far as the scale of mapping will allow. Rights of way are not shown on maps of Scotland.

The representation on this map of any other

Danger Area   Firing and Test Ranges in

BOUNDARIES

–+– –+– –+	National
–+– –+– –+	District
–·–·–·–·–	County, Unitary Authority,
	National Park

OTHER PUBLIC ACCESS

• • • •	Other route with public access
◆ ◆	National Trail, European Long
● ●	National/Regional Cycle Network
— —	Surfaced cycle route
4 8	National/Regional Cycle Network

ANTIQUITIES

+	Site of monument
· ○	Stone monument
⚔	Battlefield (with date)
☆ ''''	Visible earthwork
VILLA	Roman
Castle	Non-Roman

TOURIST INFORMATION

⛺	Camp site
🚐	Caravan site
✿	Garden
⚑	Golf course or links
i *i*	Information centre, all year / seasonal
🐦	Nature reserve
P P&R	Parking, Park and ride, all year / seasonal
✕	Picnic site
▨	Selected places of tourist interest
✆ ✆	Telephone, public / motoring organisation
⚡	Viewpoint
V	Visitor centre
!	Walks / Trails
▲	Youth hostel

ABBREVIATIONS

CG	Coastguard	P	Post office
CH	Clubhouse	PC	Town Hall, Guildhall or equivalent
MP	Milepost	PH	Public house
MS	Milestone		

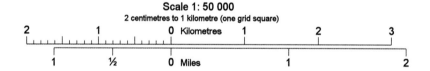

Scale 1: 50 000
2 centimetres to 1 kilometre (one grid square)

NB. Due to changes in specification there are differences on some sheets

Ordnance Survey, the OS Symbol and OS Landranger are registered trademarks of Ordnance Survey, the national mapping agency of Great Britain. Made, printed and published by Ordnance Survey, Southampton, United Kingdom. **For educational use only.**

July 2002
© Crown copyright 2002

Index